Only Once Had She Seen Him So Angry.

'We all work out our own destinies,' he said.

'Do we, though?' She had spoken the words before she realised just how he might take them.

His lip curled. He said, 'You're telling me that you didn't work out yours?'

She blushed at the implication. 'I suppose we both worked out our destinies. We weren't meant for each other, and if we had married we might now be thinking of a divorce.'

She had scarcely let the last word fall before he said harshly, 'I do not believe in divorce, and were you my wife, then you would stay that way!'

ANNE HAMPSON
currently makes her home in England, but this top romance author has travelled and lived all over the world. This variety of experience is reflected in her books, which present the ever-changing face of romance as it is found wherever people fall in love.

Dear Reader:

During the last year, many of you have written to Silhouette telling us what you like best about Silhouette Romances and, more recently, about Silhouette Special Editions. You've also told us what else you'd like to read from Silhouette. With your comments and suggestions in mind, we've developed SILHOUETTE DESIRE.

SILHOUETTE DESIREs will be on sale this June, and each month we'll bring you four new DESIREs written by some of your favorite authors—Stephanie James, Diana Palmer, Rita Clay, Suzanne Simms and many more.

SILHOUETTE DESIREs may not be for everyone, but they are for those readers who want a more sensual, provocative romance. The heroines are slightly older—women who are actively involved in their careers and the world around them. If you want to experience all the excitement, passion and joy of falling in love, then SILHOUETTE DESIRE is for you.

I'd appreciate any thoughts you'd like to share with us on new SILHOUETTE DESIRE, and I invite you to write to us at the address below:

Karen Solem
Editor-in-Chief
Silhouette Books
P.O. Box 769
New York, N.Y. 10019

ANNE HAMPSON
A Kiss and A Promise

Silhouette Romance

Published by Silhouette Books New York

America's Publisher of Contemporary Romance

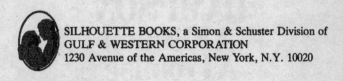

SILHOUETTE BOOKS, a Simon & Schuster Division of
GULF & WESTERN CORPORATION
1230 Avenue of the Americas, New York, N.Y. 10020

ISBN: 0-671-57151-6

First Silhouette Books printing May, 1982

10 9 8 7 6 5 4 3 2 1

All of the characters in this book are fictitious. Any resem-
blance to actual persons, living or dead, is purely coincidental.

Map by Tony Ferrara

America's Publisher of Contemporary Romance

Printed in the U.S.A.

Other Silhouette Books by Anne Hampson

Chapter One

It was with a sort of dry bitterness that Judith Sommerville read the contents of the letter for the second time.

'You've heard me speak occasionally of Helen? She wants me to take charge of her son, Petros,' remarked Judith, glancing up. Her eyes brooded as she folded the letter and put it back into its envelope.

'She's going to Greece, though—at least, that's what you told me.' The girl sitting at the sewing machine stopped what she was doing to stare at her flatmate with an odd expression. 'You'll not accept, surely?'

'I don't really know. . . .' Judith's mouth pursed thoughtfully.

Lena sighed and frowned at the same time. 'It was her brother who—er—jilted you . . . ?'

Faintly Judith smiled. 'I've survived the indignity. In fact, I'm completely cured of anything I felt for the handsome, masterful Greek who once told me I was the only girl he had ever wanted to marry.' Pausing in thought, Judith clearly remembered the thrill of those weeks when Alexis Vasilis, tall and distinguished, with dark skin and jet-black hair and eyes, had come into her life and dominated it for just over two months. It was a whirlwind affair with passion flaring almost every time they found themselves alone. He had wanted her, desperately, and in his high-handed Greek manner he had fully expected Judith to succumb to his persuasions. But she had always been determined to follow where her high ideals led, and that path was in no way the path which Alexis wanted her to take.

And so he had asked her to marry him. She accepted, and they went to London to buy the ring—a sapphire surrounded by flawless diamonds.

Alexis, at thirty-one, was the head of a shipping company originally owned by his father, who had died four years before Judith and Alexis met.

'He's a millionaire,' someone had said, and Judith could well believe it.

Judith had met Helen Voudouris, Alexis' half-sister, whose husband, Panos, owned a wine business in England. The couple lived in a gracious Tudor mansion high in the Berkshire hills, and for those few idyllic weeks Judith was familiar with the lovely house, its gardens, and its many servants.

'I love this place,' she had confided to her future sister-in-law. 'It has such a mellow atmosphere.'

'But you will be living in Greece,' Helen had reminded her. 'Alexis has a wonderful home in Delphi— Oh, you'll love it, for I'm sure I do! How I wish we could go home to Greece! But Panos has his business here, so we have to stay in this dreary country, where the sun never shines!' Helen, dark and petite with typical Greek features and a ready smile, was pouting as she spoke and Judith had laughed.

'That manner of yours doesn't affect Panos, so why bother to adopt it?'

Helen had grimaced. 'Like all Greek men, he has to be the master,' she had complained, then stared for a long while in silence at the girl who was engaged to her brother. 'You do realise that Alexis will domineer over you—that his will is the one which must prevail in your household?'

'I'm prepared for his dominance,' Judith had admitted and wondered what it was in a woman that inspired the desire to be mastered. She supposed it was the primitive instincts which still held sway, both with men and women. The man was the provider, the fighter; the woman was the one who stayed at home and cared for the children.

'Being English, though,' Helen had mused, 'you might just become fed up with being bossed about.' Although she was Greek, Helen spoke impeccable English—not like her half-brother, who had a slight accent, an accent which to Judith had seemed inordinately attractive. Alexis had been visiting his sister and her husband when he met Judith at a charity ball given by the Lord of the Manor—a lovely mansion situated only a couple of miles from his sister's home.

'I might have a few slanging matches with Alexis,' Judith had admitted with a rueful little laugh. 'But I'd much rather let him have his own way than bring about a serious quarrel.' In spite of these words a serious quarrel did, in fact, come about. Judith's onetime boyfriend, Daniel, had come home from a two-year visit to Australia; he and Judith met by accident and it was only natural that he should ask her to have lunch with him. Then he made another date, for dinner this time. Alexis was away in London on business, so Judith readily agreed to dine out with Daniel.

But it so happened that Alexis returned earlier than expected and, finding that Judith was not at home, he asked his sister and brother-in-law to dine out . . . and by some capricious trick of fate he chose the same restaurant as that chosen by Daniel.

Judith felt she would never forget that evening, especially the moment when Alexis, walking in, stopped abruptly and stared as if he could not believe the evidence before his eyes. Then anger, violent and almost uncontrollable, had taken possession of him. But somehow he had managed to be civil, though he had merely said a cold 'good evening' and passed on, urged rather hastily by his sister, who had seen everything.

The following day Alexis had been so furious, so domineering, so threatening, that Judith, no weakling despite her willingness to meet her future husband more than halfway, retaliated in a way Alexis had never for one moment believed she would.

She had given as much as she received, with the result that Alexis told her, in his customary arrogant and forthright manner, that unless she was prepared to apologise, and to give him her firm promise never to go out with another man again, he would ask her to consider the engagement at an end.

'So you don't love me?' She had stared disbelievingly for long silent moments while her heart seemed to be breaking within her. 'It was—was

10

only—desire?' So vividly she was recalling his persuasions, futile persuasions that had resulted in his asking her to marry him. 'You never loved me. It was nothing but physical desire which made you ask me to marry you?'

He had frowned then, but after a prolonged silence he had frankly admitted that she was right in her deductions. 'You're still the most desirable woman I have ever known,' he had added almost harshly, and she could see that the fact of losing her was hurting him as much as it was hurting her, but for a very different reason. 'You wouldn't be my pillow-friend, so I asked you to marry me.'

'Pillow-friend?' Judith's eyes had widened in enquiry.

'Don't be naïve!' he had snapped. 'The expression's self-explanatory!'

'How very delicate you Greeks are,' she had returned sarcastically.

And then he had stepped forward and brought her protesting body towards his. She then knew the real meaning of primitive lovemaking. Bruised and breathless when at last he released her, she would have hit him hard across the face, but he caught her hand in a ruthless grip which made her cry out with pain. Judith felt she hated him in that moment, but afterwards . . . it had taken more than a year before the pain in her heart began to ease, and over another year before she could learn to laugh again. For she had loved deeply, for the first time in her life. And she had never loved since. Minor affairs, yes, and happy times spent in male company, but she had been determined never to let her heart be touched again.

'You're very quiet, Judith,' Lena's soft voice brought Judith's mind back from its wanderings and she glanced up, stirring restlessly.

'I could do with a change of job.' She was a secretary but had also taken a nanny training course because, on leaving school, she had thought that she would like to work with children. However, her first post being a disastrous failure owing to the unwanted interest of the little boy's father, Judith had decided she would be happier in a different kind of post. Helen knew Judith was trained as a nanny, knew also that she had recently become dissatisfied with her nine-to-five job in a solicitor's musty office, for she and Judith, having become friends during the engagement, still corresponded—not often or regularly, but now and then one or the other would take it into her head to write, just so they wouldn't lose touch. It was only a fortnight since Judith had sent a letter saying she was unsettled in her job and wished she could find something more congenial.

'I can't quite understand why Helen wants to go back to Greece,' said Lena, and Judith answered at once.

'I think I mentioned that she often used to become homesick. Well, as Panos has just partnered up with another wine merchant in Portugal and intends to go there for about a year to get the business running smoothly, Helen asked if he'd mind her going home.'

'She didn't want to go to Portugal with him?' asked Lena frowningly.

'She mentioned in her next-to-last letter that she was more homesick than ever before and was thinking of suggesting to her husband that she and their child take a long holiday in Greece.'

'She has relatives there—other than Alexis, I mean?'

Judith nodded her dark head. 'Her mother's still living—Helen and Alexis had different fathers, and both are dead. There are several brothers and sisters, as well, and lots of cousins. You know how it is with Greeks; they all seem to have large families.'

A profound silence followed before Lena asked perceptively, 'You wish you were a member of a large family, don't you?'

Again Judith nodded. 'An only child is a lonely one. There's no truer saying than that. I was looking forward to becoming a member of a large family.'

'Alexis' family.' Lena spoke to herself; she had momentarily returned her attention to the skirt she was making, a cotton skirt, flared and short, which she hoped to be wearing that evening, when she went to the local hop with her boyfriend.

'Yes, his family. I don't know if they'd have taken to me,' added Judith, having paused after the first sentence. 'However, it wasn't to be.'

'But if you accept this job, you'll be meeting him again.'

'After four years.' Alexis would be thirty-five now, she reflected, and she herself was twenty-six.

'He isn't married?'

'No. Helen would have mentioned it if he was.'

'Engaged?'

Judith's grey eyes became thoughtful. 'Helen

13

did mention in her last letter that there was a girl. Camille something-or-other. French—well, part French and part English. Perhaps he'll marry her.'

'If he can't get what he wants without,' Lena was swift to return with a grimace.

Judith coloured slightly as the words brought back a memory. 'I daresay he has had many pillow-friends during the past four years.'

'And will have even more when he is married, I expect.'

At that Judith frowned. 'I know that most Greeks are unfaithful, but I never believed Alexis would be like that. I feel sure that once he is married, he'll not bother with other women.'

'An idealist!' Lena sighed a little as she looked at her friend, taking in the mass of gleaming dark brown hair, the serious grey eyes, the facial lines and contours that could not be faulted, nor could the skin, peach coloured and finely textured. Her forehead was high, unlined, her mouth full and generous. She had a lovely figure, and she possessed an unusually sublime air of distinction. 'You're terribly naïve, Judith.'

'I'm twenty-six,' she reminded her friend.

'I still say you're naïve.'

Judith shrugged and changed the subject. 'Helen obviously doesn't like minding her own baby.'

'Most rich mothers have a nanny these days.' Lena paused a moment, becoming occupied with pinning up the hem of the skirt. 'How old is the child? I had the impression that he was rather more than a baby.'

'Yes. He's three and a half years old.'

'You've never seen him?'

'No. Helen and I don't visit one another.'

'I expect she felt awful—about the broken engagement, I mean?'

'She was upset, because she and I had become friends.' Judith fell silent, a thoughtful expression in her eyes. 'We had both looked forward to the time when we'd be related—sisters.' A sigh escaped her, but there was no pain anymore. No, that had healed long ago and she knew that she had nothing to fear from an encounter with the man she had once loved. She was immune to his charms—and in any case, it would appear that he was well settled with this Camille.

'Well,' said Lena after another silence, 'have you made up your mind to accept and go for a sojourn in Greece?'

'I shall think seriously about it,' returned Judith. 'I feel I have come to a—well—sort of crossroads in my life and career. This job I'm in isn't going to lead anywhere important. I want to find something with greater prospects.'

Her friend shook her head, a little gesture that seemed to denote both sadness and impatience. 'You sound as if you're fully resigned to spinsterhood,' Lena said almost irritably. 'And as for prospects—what sort of prospects will this post of temporary nanny afford you?'

'None, I admit, but it'll be a break, make a change—and that's what I want at present.'

Lena threaded a needle to sew up the hem by hand. 'You've been restless for weeks.'

'It's Mr. Holding. He seems determined to find fault with almost everything I do.'

'Take no notice,' her friend advised. 'He's a

miserable old bachelor who ought to be thinking of retiring.'

'He has four years yet before he retires.' *I shall then be thirty*, Judith mused—*thirty and perhaps out of a job*. No one could guarantee that the new department manager would agree to keep his predecessor's secretary. He might have one he wished to bring with him.

To Judith's amazement, the meeting with Alexis proved to be nostalgic; she was recalling numerous incidents of pleasure, remembering his passionate kisses, his almost overbearing masterfulness. He seemed not to have aged at all, with the additional years having caused no noticeable physical changes, although his manner was somewhat changed. His smile was delayed, not spontaneous, as once it had been; his attitude seemed rather more austere than Judith remembered it, and there was about him an air of polish and arrogance which served as a supplement to the self-confidence which, at times, she had found more than a little disconcerting.

She was immune, she had told herself . . . but she was wrong. *I'm still affected by you*, she thought silently, and she was staggered by the admission. She gritted her teeth, told herself she was merely being sentimental and melodramatic.

Little did she know that Alexis was thinking to himself: *I still desire you*.

They had arrived at the villa only an hour ago. Judith had not expected Helen to be staying with Alexis, but to be living in another house altogether. However, she was immune. So why care that she was to stay in her former fiancé's lovely

16

white villa overlooking the Sacred Precincts of the sun-god Apollo?

And now, as she stood just inside the door after coming down to look for Helen, she realised that her immunity against Alexis' kind of attraction was proving easily broken down. Neither one spoke for a full minute and the silence was tense, profoundly disturbing for Judith. Indescribable waves of emotion were passing through her; she had the sensation of something strong and binding. It was to her as if the whole world revolved round them both, with nothing to interfere with the rhythmic revolutions. Primordial and earth binding their relationship at this quiet, tense, and profound moment in time. It all seemed to have been planned a millennium ago, with only the Supreme Being in control. She shut her eyes against the unnatural sensation, then opened them and tried to sound light and normal. 'Hello, Alexis! How are you?'

'*Yassoo*, Judith! I am well, and . . . happy.'

She looked swiftly at him, wondering at the hesitation. She said softly, 'I hope my being here won't inconvenience you. When Helen asked me to be nanny to little Petros, I naturally concluded that she was to have a home of her own.'

'It was considered, but we decided it wasn't necessary. I have more than enough room here.'

'Your mother doesn't live with you?' Judith glanced past him to where a *vraga*-clad gardener was setting up a sprinkler on the lawn. Flowers abounded out there—hibiscus, oleander, bougainvillaea, and numerous others. A fountain played, seen through a white marble arch

17

supported by statues—Athena at one side, and Artemis at the other.

'No. She prefers her own home still. There might come a time when she'll consent to giving it up, but certainly not while she is fit and well.'

'Is she very old?' Questions and answers. They were both talking just for the sake of avoiding another intensely emotional silence.

'In her late sixties; that's not old these days.'

'She lives close by?'

'About a mile away.'

'Alone?' It was then that Judith saw the mocking smile which at one time had either sent her into confusion or brought a militant sparkle to her eyes.

'Tell me about yourself,' Alexis invited, beckoning towards a chair facing the window. 'What have you been doing all this time?'

Judith thought: no antagonism, no recollections of the parting, which for her had meant months of heartbreak. They might never have been engaged, never kissed . . . or made love with such passion that at times they had almost reached the point beyond which there was no return.

She told him about her job and how, recently, she had become dissatisfied with it. 'When Helen made this offer, it seemed heaven-sent,' Judith remarked, 'although at first I wasn't quite sure if I'd accept.'

'But you did,' slowly and thoughtfully. 'And here you are—here *we* are, meeting again, in my country. You'll enjoy your stay, Judith. This is a particularly wonderful part of Greece, as you will admit as soon as you've been to the Sanctuary.'

The Sanctuary of Apollo, beloved son of Zeus and Leto and brother of Artemis. Apollo was born on the tiny island of Delos and, symbolized on occasions by a dolphin, he gave the name 'Delphi' to the most holy place of ancient Greece, the place of his Sanctuary, where suppliants came from all parts of the known world to seek advice from the Oracle. And now, as she gazed from the window of the beautiful villa, which could have been her home, but for that fateful evening she had spent with her former boy-friend, Judith thought of those ancient times when men put their full trust in the Delphic Oracle, never doubting the advice given them through the lips of the priestess and interpreted by the priest.

There seemed to be a celestial quality about the site, even when viewed from this distance; Judith could feel it. Perhaps she showed something in her face, because she heard Alexis say, very quietly so that she only just caught the words, 'Your mind is adrift. Where have you taken it?'

A smile curved her lips. 'I was thinking about the Oracle, and the faith it inspired in people.' She paused, not quite sure what she wanted to say. 'Many vital problems were solved and questions answered. So simple were the solutions. . . .'

She trailed off and Alexis finished for her: 'If only life today were half as simple. In other words, if we could consult the Oracle about the problems with which we are so often beset. Yes, how very comfortable life would be.'

Was he mocking her? He appeared to be serious enough, but with Alexis one never quite caught his mood. He was able to hide his feelings behind the dark depths of those fathomless Greek eyes of his.

Judith said, in order to break the silence that was falling between them, 'I cannot think that you have many problems, Alexis.'

His eyes flickered momentarily. 'Every one of us has problems of one kind or another,' he commented at length. 'I have my business; you have your job.'

She nodded and sighed unconsciously. 'I don't know what I shall do when Helen no longer wants me.'

'She might decide to keep you on even when she returns to England. I never did understand why she was willing to look after Petros herself when she was in England, but now that she is here she needs a nanny.' An underlying edge to his voice puzzled her.

It was exactly what had occurred to Judith, and all she could think of was that Helen, away from the vigilant eyes of her husband, intended to have a little freedom. Time would tell, of course. Judith admitted she could be wrong in her guess. She changed the subject, asking Alexis about his business, and if he had launched any more ships since the one she had read about last year.

'We launched a rather special cruise ship three months ago,' he told her. 'It's called the *Santa Maura*.'

'Named after an island, isn't it?'

Alexis nodded his head. He seemed more than a little interested in her now, and she felt the keen vigilance of his gaze. 'We call it Lefkas, too.'

'Tell me about the ship.' Judith had no idea why she wanted to keep him with her. She ought to be looking for Helen, who presumably had Petros with her somewhere in the garden. 'Is she very large?'

'Not too large at all; twelve thousand tons.'

'So she carries about four hundred passengers?'

'We intend to keep it down to three hundred, or perhaps a few more. As I said, it's rather special.' He stopped a moment, and then, 'I shall be taking a short cruise on her myself later in the season. You and Helen must come, too.'

Judith said nothing. The very idea of a romantic cruise was undoubtedly exciting, and yet she knew she must refuse when the time came—unless, of course, Helen insisted, in which case she would be forced to go, since little Petros would be in her charge, and Helen would not go on the cruise without him. Judith wondered if Camille would go, too, and a sense of weight crept over her.

'I must go and find Helen,' she said flatly. 'She'll be wondering what I'm doing.'

'She'll expect you to be unpacking.' Alexis moved with the ease and grace Judith had once found so exciting, his body slim and pliant, narrow waisted, broad shouldered. She watched the way he carried himself, with his head proudly set, his long legs crossing the room in a mere three or four strides. He was at the cocktail cabinet when he swung round. 'What will you have?' he asked, opening the doors.

'Oh—only a glass of lemonade, please.' She was faintly taken aback at his action, as she had expected him to let her go once she had decided

21

to do so. Instead, he seemed as anxious to keep her as she was to stay. She accepted the tall crystal glass from him and their fingers touched. The tiny electric shock brought colour to her cheeks. Alexis smiled down at her with that hint of mockery in his eyes.

'Almost like old times, eh?' His voice was low and yet whimsical, like the tilt of his lip at one corner. How sure of himself he was! And how perceptive. He knew full well he was disconcerting her—and he was deriving supreme enjoyment from the knowledge!

'Almost, but not quite.' Judith's voice was brittle.

'How is it that you're not married?' The question she had been expecting, and wondering why it hadn't come before now.

'I'm not interested in men.'

'But men must have been interested in you,' he observed as he subjected her to an overall visual examination before allowing his eyes to linger on the delicate upsweep of her firm, round breasts. She blushed more hotly and heard him laugh, quietly, as if to himself. But it riled her and her pointed little chin shot up.

'What's so funny?' she almost snapped. 'I can't think I've said or done anything that's in any way amusing.'

He ignored that as, turning, he poured himself a drink. When he turned again she saw that his eyes were veiled.

'Have you any real idea as to why my sister is here?' he enquired at last. Only then did she realise just how long had been his hesitation before putting forth the question. Judith flashed him a glance and frowned.

'You sound as if—as if . . .' She trailed off as her mind worked to find just what she wanted to say. 'Surely she and Panos are not—not thinking of parting?'

'Why so surprised?' Alexis asked caustically. 'Divorce is common these days.'

Judith shook her head vigourously. 'No! I can't believe their marriage is breaking up.'

'It hasn't broken up, if that is what you really mean. But it's on the rocks, as the saying goes.' He tilted his glass and seemed to swallow more of the liquid than he should have.

'Helen doesn't seem upset— Oh, surely you are mistaken!' she cried in distress. 'Helen is so nice, and Panos—well, he's bossy and he doesn't fuss over her, but I'm sure he loves her.'

Alexis smiled faintly down at her. 'How should you be able to express an opinion?' he wanted to know. 'Their lives are private, and who knows how much or how little they get on one another's nerves?'

She frowned again, more darkly this time. 'You seem so casual about it,' she accused. 'Aren't you troubled?'

'In a way.' His mouth seemed to tighten.

'Well, then, aren't you going to try to do something to keep them together?'

Alexis lifted one eyebrow. 'Neither one would thank me for interfering. They'll work out their own destinies, just as we all do.'

'Do we, though? Do we all work out our own destinies?' She had spoken the words before she realised just how he might take them.

His lip curled. He said, after taking another drink, 'You're telling me that you didn't work out your own destiny?'

She blushed at the implication, but her voice was steady as she replied, 'I suppose we both worked out our destinies. We weren't meant for each other, and if we had married it might have been the two of us who were thinking of a divorce.'

She had scarcely let the last word fall before he said harshly, 'I do not believe in divorce, and were you my wife, then you would stay that way!'

Judith stared. Only on that fateful evening had she seen Alexis looking like this—looking like one of the pagan gods, with that stone-cold, level gaze and those tight lips. Judith turned away, confused and angry with herself for being the cause of this little scene.

'You don't believe in divorce, and yet you're so casual about the situation between Helen and Panos,' she said at last.

'That is their affair. You were talking about us.'

'Then I think we had better change the subject,' Judith suggested and, turning, saw the glint appear in the chill directness of his gaze. 'I don't mean to be rude,' she hastily told him. 'I merely felt that the conversation was profitless.'

It was strange, but there was a certain intimacy about this whole situation, she thought, recalling how, when she had visualised the meeting, she had seen only a sort of compelled civility between them, a coolness as both remembered the quarrel which had brought about their separation. She looked at him, saw that he was still angry, but when he spoke it was in a quiet tone as he asked her what she was thinking.

'I was thinking about us,' she answered frankly, 'about this meeting between us, which I had imagined would be so different from what it is.' Her eyes were wide and beautiful, faintly shadowed because at this moment she was thinking of what might have been—marriage, children, happiness, and love.

Strangely, he held her gaze as he said, 'You were expecting it to be cool and conventional?'

She nodded, batting her lashes. 'Yes, I was expecting it to be something like that.'

Alexis moved closer, and for some reason she knew fear. Rather unsteadily, she rose to her feet after placing her glass on the small table at her elbow. She had no idea why she had risen, or why she should be feeling tense and afraid.

'Judith,' she heard him say in an unfathomable tone of voice, 'why did you come here?'

She blinked because this was not a question she had expected. 'It was at Helen's request. You know that.'

The dark eyes, cold and level, seemed all at once to hold contempt, not unmingled with mockery. He seemed to be measuring his words as he said, 'It wasn't a natural course, though, was it?'

'What do you mean?' Unconsciously she had taken a backwards step towards the door. 'I don't know what you are getting at.'

'Under the circumstances, and in view of the way we parted, it was not natural for you to agree to come here. On the contrary, it was more conceivable that you would have instantly refused my sister's offer.'

A flood of colour darkened her face as she grasped his meaning. 'Are you implying that I jumped at the chance of meeting you again? What an opinion you have of yourself! You always were pompous and self-opinionated, but this—! My God, if that is what you think, then you can just think again! I had no wish for a meeting, but I knew that it must come. I was prepared for the cool, conventional meeting you have just mentioned—and nothing more!'

'Living here, in my home, you knew something more must occur—'

'I never expected to be living in your home!' she broke in fiercely. 'I naturally assumed that Helen would have her own house.'

'How could she? Her home is in England.' Cynical the tone and the expression in his eyes. 'No, Judith, you seized the opportunity for a reconciliation—'

'I did not! I hate you for reaching a conclusion like that!'

'Hate?' with a lift of his brows. He moved with the lithe agility of a jungle cat, and before she knew what he was about, he had grasped her wrist and she was jerked, roughly, to his hard and sinewed body. A struggle ensued, fierce and prolonged, as Judith fought for freedom from the steel hawsers of his arms. At last she sagged, eyes filled with tears as his hard, demanding mouth closed on hers in a kiss that totally lacked respect. His hands roamed, one along the length of her spine, and the other to take one breast, enclosing it possessively. The warm, sensual caresses of both hands communicated his desire; she tried desperately to resist the temptation he was subjecting her to, but she had no defence against the heady, emotional pleasure—erotic pleasure—he was arousing within her, and she was soon gripped by the longing to reciprocate. Yet still she fought, mentally, the desire of the flesh and did manage for a time to remain like a log in his embrace. But she should have known from past experience that he would conquer in the end. She found herself pressing close, curving her supple frame to meet the virility of his. She blushed to feel his hardness and yet pressed even closer still, until it seemed their two bodies were melding together as one.

'Your thighs are soft and wonderful.' he murmured in a throaty bass tone, his sensuous lips, warm and moist, touching the soft, delicate flesh of the breast he had uncovered almost without her being aware of it.

'Alexis . . . let me go. . . .' The appeal was so weak that he gave a low laugh and kissed her more passionately than ever. She thrilled to the strength of a mouth that bruised while it possessed, to the warmth of hands smoothly caressing, to the virile body that was so easily conquering hers. Flames, fierce and relentless, consumed them both until it seemed that, as on so many occasions in the past, they would be carried by blind passion almost to the point of no return.

Sanity came to them both at the same time. Judith cried out her protest even as she found herself being released. Alexis stood over her, his hands busy with her blouse buttons, his eyes mocking and victorious. She averted her head against the kind of look which seemed only to insult.

She would go home, she decided—yes, that was the only course open to her now that this had happened.

Chapter Two

Helen stood in her bedroom staring at Judith, who had just come to her. She was standing just inside the door of the elegant mauve and white room, her face pale but composed, her eyes steady with determination.

'You can't leave me!' cried Helen for the third time in less than a minute. 'You came here to look after Petros—you know I need you—'

'I don't know any such thing,' interrupted Judith patiently. 'You looked after your child when you were in England, so why can't you do it now?'

'Simply because I don't want to!'

It was Judith's turn to stare, for here was an altogether different side of Helen's makeup, one she, Judith, had never realised could exist. Still, she mused reflectively, she really knew very little about the girl, having merely corresponded with her on occasions, not very often, since the parting.

'What has happened to make you like this?' asked Judith at last, and Helen, her dark face set and tense, declared frankly that she was sick of being the subjugated wife. She wanted a life of her own, the life she had missed when she was forced into marriage with Panos. 'But surely you wanted to marry him,' said Judith when at length the older girl paused.

'In Greece, marriages are arranged—'

'Not now, surely—not in these enlightened times, and especially not with people of your status.'

'*My* marriage was arranged and I obeyed my parents, as every dutiful daughter in Greece is expected to, but I know now that I ought to have had the courage to rebel!' She turned away and moved towards the window, absently putting out a hand to grip the long silken tassel which controlled the drawing of the curtains.

Judith watched her as she let the threads run through her fingers. She said at last, 'Are you and Panos going to get a divorce?'

'We haven't yet made up our minds.'

'There's . . . someone else?'

Helen nodded her head. 'We met when he was in London on business—with Panos. He's Greek; lives in Langadia.'

'That's not far from Delphi.' Judith spoke mechanically, almost to herself. She was shocked by the idea that Helen, mother of a young child, could have found someone else. But she kept her feelings to herself since, after all, it was none of her business. 'So that is why you want a nanny for Petros—so that you'll be free to—er—have this affair?'

'Put it how you like!'

'I was merely stating a fact. What you do, Helen, is entirely your own affair, and if you want a nanny for Petros, then obviously you'll have one—but it won't be me.'

Helen swung round. 'What exactly happened? All you've said up till now is that you and Alexis cannot live in the same house.'

'And that's all I intend saying.' Judith's voice

was quiet but determined, this after several days of considering.

A sigh of exasperation broke the silence. 'It's a rotten trick, to leave me now,' complained Helen wrathfully. She was far from pretty in her anger, thought Judith as she looked at her. But her hair was still lovely, black, like her brother's, and gleaming, and her skin, clear and unlined, glowed with health. 'Please stay with me, Judith.' Helen's voice had changed; she was now begging Judith to change her mind about leaving. 'I shall see that my brother doesn't make himself objectionable to you— I suppose it *is* that? He was nasty because of what happened all that time ago?'

If that were all, then she could stay, thought Judith, but grimly she was living through that scene last week when she had come so close to losing all she had held dear, her chastity. She was old-fashioned enough to want to save herself for the man she might one day marry. Yes, old-fashioned and perhaps foolish, since life was for living, and undoubtedly a girl could have a good time if she were willing to forego her ideals.

'I can't stay, Helen—I'm sorry,' she said at last.

'But why?' No answer from Judith, and Helen flounced past her and went running along the hall towards the room which Judith knew was Alexis' study.

'What—!' Judith gave a deep sigh and left the room, to wander in the garden, her mind in chaos from all that was happening in so short a time: the scene with Alexis; the decision to go back to England, instead of staying to be nanny to Petros; the anxiety of getting another job; the knowledge of trouble between Helen and her husband. . . . It was no wonder her mind was in turmoil, she thought as she wandered away from the house, unconsciously putting some distance between it and her, between the occupants who were at this moment probably quarrelling.

'What shall I do?'

The question staggered Judith; she had made her decision, so the question was not necessary. Yet it repeated itself all the time she was walking. She came to a little arbour, hidden from the villa, and she sat down on the rustic seat, trying to relax. And after a while she succeeded, lazily becoming aware of the peace, the tranquillity. She could see the lovely Temple of Zeus gleaming in the sunshine—not the Temple, she thought sadly, but only what remained of it. Earthquakes, vandalism, and the relentless forces of nature had wrought havoc with the original structure and all that remained were a few stately columns and some scattered bases. But the peace was there, the sacredness of it all. An ache filled her throat, the sort of tight, choking sensation which appears when the tide of ecstasy becomes a deluge that drowns all other emotions and takes the heart and mind to a realm beyond man's understanding. Such was the impression which the Sanctuary gave out, and Judith was profoundly aware of it as she sat there, receptive, and appreciative of all the ancient Greek world had given to mankind.

On sudden impulse she rose and walked the distance to the sacred site and there sat on a fallen column, the sun in her hair, its warmth

31

penetrating the chill that had crept into her heart. She looked up as a shadow fell before her, and somehow was not as surprised as she ought to have been at seeing Alexis standing there, his having come quietly, as if, like Judith, he were afraid of disturbing the slumbering gods or, more likely, their spirits.

'Has Helen been talking to you?' She just had to speak and she did it in haste. Alexis nodded as he sat down opposite her, his hands clasped in front of him. So distinguished! Even in the open-necked shirt and the denim trews.

'She tells me you are leaving, even before you've taken up your duties.'

'Is there any need to explain?' she countered, challenging him with the bright sparkle in her eyes.

'You take life far too seriously—always did,' he began when she interrupted him.

'Because I'm not modern?'

The dark eyes roved over her and he smiled faintly, mockingly. 'Because you are not realistic.'

'You'd still like me for your pillow-friend, wouldn't you?'

'Of course. I thought that would have been made clear to you a short while ago, when we almost made l——'

'Helen was right when she told you I was leaving,' cut in Judith hastily. 'I've made up my mind and nothing will alter it.'

'Stubborn wench.' The accent in his voice seemed rather more pronounced than usual, and she felt he was smothering anger. 'I want you to stay,' he added matter-of-factly, and Judith gave a gasp of disbelief.

'You think it is as easy as that?' she exclaimed. 'I said you were pompous and—'

'Let us keep the conversation civil,' he admonished. 'There is no need for abuse or criticism. I have said, I want you to stay.'

'The reason?' Judith looked interestedly at him, waiting for him to answer her.

'Petros.' The brevity of his reply caused a puzzled frown to crease her brow.

'Petros?' she echoed. 'And . . . ?'

'His need for someone like you. He's about to face an upheaval in his young life that could have disastrous results. You could prevent his being hurt too much.'

'He's a mere baby; he'll not know anything about it.'

'He's three and a half and highly intelligent. He loves both his parents, needs both his parents. Even now, he will be missing his father. And if his mother is absent from his life, as well—' Alexis spread his hands. 'I believe that someone like you, sympathetic and understanding, will help him to remain on his present even keel—'

'But you've just said he's already missing his father.'

'Not keenly, because it's early days. His father has been away before, but never for any length of time. Petros is soon going to ask where his daddy is.'

'I can't be a substitute, can I?'

'You can be tender with him; he'll soon be relying on you, gaining affection for you. Children are like that; they respond to kindness. Petros is not going to be hurt, Judith, and that is why I am asking you to stay.'

She shook her head, but weakly. 'I can't—'

'I'll not molest you,' he promised. And, a smile curving the fine, well-sculptured lips, 'You know, my child, you also enjoyed our little interlude— No, don't you dare deny it! I'm not a fool—'

'Because you've had plenty of experience!' she could not help breaking in to say.

'Precisely.'

She coloured. 'Why must men brag of their conquests?' she snapped.

'I wasn't bragging of mine. I was merely agreeing with an assumption you had made.'

'A correct one, obviously,' she returned tartly.

He drew a breath of asperity. 'Can we get back to the business of your post as nanny?'

'I have relinquished the post.'

'You can't do that. You have to give at least a month's notice.'

She bit her lip. She had thought of that, but assumed she would be allowed to leave at once. 'I can't stay a month,' she began.

'You can and you will—and longer.' So determined was the tone, and imperious.

Judith's eyes flamed. 'You can't make me— Oh, yes, the month! I suppose you can keep me to that, but not a moment longer will I stay!'

He remained silent. Watching him closely, Judith gained the annoying impression that he was congratulating himself on having gained a victory over her. Well, just let him wait! She meant what she said when she told him she would not stay a day longer than the month.

The silence continued, and after a few moments she was content to sit here, enjoying the warm sunshine, the peace, and to her surprise she was even glad of the company of the distinguished man opposite her, even though there was scant friendliness between them.

He looked at her without expression; she glanced away, profoundly conscious of her surroundings: the wild and lonely aspect, for there were no tourists within her view, the absence of any living thing besides themselves—but for a flitting bird-wing flashing colour and then gone, and now the scuffle of a wary lizard in the bracken at her feet.

'It's so remote from man. . . .' She spoke aloud to herself, her eyes wide and limpid and filled with the appreciation of what was spread out before them—the Temple and the Treasuries, the massive Theatre rising to the sky, the towering peaks of Mount Parnassas, the Gorge of the Pleistos opening dramatically onto the Sacred Plain of Amphissa, a veritable sea of ten thousand ancient olive trees, their foliage silver in the glowing light of the sun. A pack-donkey ambled along at the base of the foothills, his black-clad owner trudging with weary persistence beside him. Judith's eyes wandered again to the distant scene, to the blue Gulf of Corinth, a dazzling expanse of water caressed by the rain of gold which was the sunlight.

'It's time I was getting back.' Alexis' calm voice severed the train of Judith's thoughts, which had been on the ancient past, when suppliants came from near and far to worship at the shrine of the sun-god and to seek advice from the Oracle. 'I have work to do.' Alexis rose as he spoke, his eyes never leaving her face. 'So it's settled,' he said as he straightened up to an incredible height above her. 'You're staying to take care of Petros.'

'For a month, yes,' she agreed, though reluctantly. Far better to leave now before added danger came her way.

'We shall see about that,' tersely as he began to walk away. She sat there for a few minutes, to allow him to get away. Then she rose and was about to move when a coin rolled along a flagstone and came to rest by her foot.

'Sorry!' An insouciant grin accompanied the brief apology as the young man stooped to retrieve his ten-drachma piece.

Judith smiled weakly and was walking away when the voice said, 'Are you on holiday? You look lonely. Want company for lunch?'

She turned, taking the man's measure, absorbing the fact that he was very young, not more than twenty-three, that he had fair wavy hair, clear skin, and blue eyes that laughed at her as they went from her face right over her body to her feet.

'No, thank you,' she answered without much expression.

'No? Are you on holiday?' he asked again.

'I have a job here.' Her instinct had been to ignore him, but she felt that would be churlish because he was obviously quite harmless.

'A job? Lucky you! You're English, though— from the south.'

'I'm English,' she returned.

'Do have lunch with me—I ought not to have come alone. I knew I'd hate it, but when my mate was rushed off to have his appendix out I didn't feel like cancelling the holiday. However, it was a mistake.' He paused and looked so forlorn that she felt sorry for him and said she would have lunch with him, but she had to go back to the villa first.

'I haven't really started work yet,' she confessed. 'The little boy I'm nanny to went off a couple of hours ago to see his aunt—one of his young cousins came for him. So I'm free. However, I feel I ought to go back and tell my employer what I am doing for the next hour or so.'

He walked with her; they exchanged a little information and she learnt that his name was Leslie Brockhurst and he came from Birmingham. He worked in a solicitor's office, worked from nine to five and hated every moment of it.

'I wish I could get a job like you,' he ended with a sigh.

'What—as a nanny?'

He laughed but went on to say, 'Why not? This business of Women's Lib and all that. I daresay that little boy would be very happy to have me mind him all day.'

'Perhaps,' was all Judith replied to that, and a short while later she was telling Helen that she would stay for a month.

'Alexis made you?'

A glint entered Judith's grey eyes. 'Nobody makes me do anything I don't want to do,' she said shortly.

'I'm sorry. What I meant was that my brother has influenced you.'

'He reminded me that I must give a month's notice.' Judith's tone was still crisp. 'I could go, of course, but as it isn't the correct thing to do, I shall stay and work out my notice.'

'You haven't given me notice.'

'Then I give it now!'

'Perhaps you'll reconsider eventually.'

'No chance.'

'I must look for someone else, then?'

It would be wise, if you haven't any intention of looking after Petros yourself.' A pause, and then: 'Seeing that he isn't here, I have accepted an offer to have my lunch out.'

'You have?' Helen's eyes opened wide. 'You've made a friend already?'

'I have met a young man, yes.'

'Not picked him up, I hope.'

'I think you could call it that,' returned Judith, well aware that she was giving Helen a shock. 'We met on the site by Apollo's Temple—very romantic.' What was she doing? This was not like her. Perhaps, she thought afterwards, she had been hoping that Helen would consider her unfit to care for her son and so let her go at once. No such thing happened, and resignation was strong within her when, half an hour later, she was sitting opposite Leslie in a very charming little *cafeneion* where the tables were outside, shaded by vines and where two men were sitting apart playing *bouzouki* music, big smiles on their brown faces, smiles which revealed bright gold fillings. These fillings were one way of saving up, Judith had already learnt. The men had gold fillings, whilst the women usually bought bangles. Judith and Leslie had freshly baked wholemeal bread, the typical Greek *mávro psomi* baked in an outside oven; they had olives like plums; *halloómi*—the delightfully smooth cheese made from goats' milk; and tomatoes as large as apples. For the main course Judith had *soovlákia*, while Leslie chose *bar-*

38

bouni, the delicious red mullet freshly caught, then cooked in spices and garnished with crispy fried potatoes and mushrooms. For dessert they had freshly picked figs, and the whole was washed down with *áspro krasi,* a fruity white wine made locally.

'That was lovely!' enthused Leslie, leaning back and looking rather more than replete. 'I love Greek food, don't you?'

'I like what I've had,' she returned with a smile. 'I've not been here very long, so I haven't sampled much of the food yet.'

'Try the fish, and the kebabs,' he recommended. 'They're mouth watering, I can tell you!'

He seemed so young, yet refreshing after the old fogeys she had been working with in the office. It was nice to have company of her own age, and when he suggested she meet him that evening, she said she'd get away if she could.

'I won't promise, but if I can get away I'll meet you at the Sanctuary.'

'By the Temple?'

She nodded. 'Yes. If I'm not there by half past eight, I won't be coming.'

He frowned; she saw how disappointed he was even at the idea that she might not come.

'How will I get in touch again, if you don't turn up?'

'Can I phone you?'

'I'm staying at the Artemis.'

'I'll give you a ring in the morning. What time will suit you?'

'Any time between eight and half past nine.'

She laughed at his expression. 'Don't look so glum. I might be there this evening. I shall certainly try.'

'This child—surely you won't have to stay by his bedside, for heaven's sake!'

'I think he will sleep, and if so I shall ask if I can leave him. There are several servants in the house, and his uncle. His mother might even be in; I don't know for sure.' Would Helen go out with her man friend? she wondered. Such an assignation would provide gossip, and she did wonder just how Alexis would take it.

'I must be off,' she was saying very soon. 'Petros might be home sooner than I expect.'

It was after five when the little boy arrived back, brought by the fourteen-year-old who had come for him. Petros was a tall, lively child, uninhibited, and he spoke excellent English, as well as Greek. Bilingual at three and a half. It made Judith feel lazy, for she had never learnt a foreign language in depth; her knowledge of anything except English was limited to the French she had learnt at school.

'Hello, Petros.' She smiled as she greeted him and his own spontaneous smile came swiftly. 'Have you enjoyed your afternoon?'

'A lot! My Aunt Souphoula lets me sit on her knee and she sings to me!'

'He's spoilt.' This from his cousin, Maria, whose voice was faintly contemptuous. 'You see, he doesn't come often, so everyone fusses over him and he likes it!'

'Everyone doesn't fuss over me!' he objected and stuck his tongue out at her.

'If Uncle Alexis sees you do that, he'll spank you,' warned his cousin. 'And I hope he does see you!' she added as a parting shot.

Judith looked at him sternly. 'That was very rude, Petros.'

'What was rude?' The cool enquiry made Judith spin round, to find herself looking up into the expressionless face of the man to whom she was once engaged.

Maria, who had been about to leave, swung round and said, 'Petros stuck out his tongue at me.'

'Telling tales!' Petros glowered at her. 'I didn't stick my tongue out!'

'And now he's telling fibs.' Maria's command of English amazed Judith, for there was only the merest hint of an alien accent in her voice.

'So you stuck your tongue out.' Alexis, tall and stern and appearing really threatening, beckoned to his nephew, who came to him so quickly that it was plain he held his uncle in awe. 'You had better tell Maria you are sorry.'

Petros' mouth went tight and it seemed that he would defy his uncle. But caution prevailed and after another small hesitation he turned to her and said, 'I'm sorry, Maria.' But the look he gave her was in no way reflective of contrition.

'And the fib?' asked Alexis sternly.

'I am sorry about that, as well.'

'As well—what?'

'Uncle Alexis.' The boy's face was reddening.

Judith took hold of his hand and said softly, 'Shall we go up to the nursery now, Petros, and have our tea?'

'Yes, I'm very hungry.'

'Is Helen about?' asked Judith. They were in the flower-bedecked hall and one of the maids, Androula, was just finishing watering the plants. She glanced up as if she would speak, then changed her mind.

'I have an idea she's gone out.'

'You're not sure?'

'No, I'm not sure.'

It was then that Androula intervened. 'Kyria Voudouris went out one hour ago and said she would not be back until very late, so I was not to wait up to give her any supper.'

Judith, watching Alexis, saw his mouth tighten. But his voice was low and polite as he said, 'Thank you, Androula.'

'Will it be all right if I go out this evening?' Judith asked a little anxiously. She did not think that Alexis was in the mood for granting favours. He was plainly furious with Helen, even though he had earlier agreed that what she did was her business and no-one else's.

'And leave Petros, you mean?'

'I would like to dine out, with a friend. I needn't go until half past eight. Petros will be asleep by then and one of the maids can attend to him if he should wake and want anything.'

'It is your job to look after Petros,' was his chill reply. 'No, I'm afraid you can't be free this evening. Were Helen in, it would be different.'

Silence, long and profound.

'I would like to know what my working hours are,' she managed at last through the pall of anger swiftly possessing her.

'You want to work set hours?' He shook his head in a way that only added to her fury. 'Nannies have no set hours.'

'They are not on duty twenty-four hours a day!'

'Who is this friend you have made so quickly?' he demanded, and now Judith's chin lifted and there was a militant sparkle in her eyes as she answered him in crisp and fluid tones.

'That, Alexis, is my business. I refuse to discuss my friends with you—or with anyone else, for that matter. I would like to be with him this evening, and I feel it's unfair of you to try to keep me in when you know as well as I that Petros will sleep the moment he goes to bed—and that is at half past seven.' She paused a moment and then went on: 'I am going to insist, Alexis, simply because you are unreasonable—' A snap of his hand halted her and she coloured up with embarrassment.

'It is not unreasonable for me to expect you to do your duty, which is what you are being paid for. I am the one who will insist,' he added imperiously. 'I insist that you stay in in case Petros should wake and require attention.'

Seething, but unable to see how she could argue against such a domineering manner, Judith shot him a glowering look and, holding her young charge firmly by the hand, she went through the hall, along the wide corridor, and entered the nursery. Androula was there already, setting the table with things she had brought in on a tray.

'Will there be anything else, Miss?' she enquired respectfully.

Judith shook her head. 'No, Androula, thank you. We have more than sufficient there.' For herself, she couldn't have eaten if she tried. Anger choked her, blocking her throat, affecting her nerves. The sooner the month was up, the better pleased she would be!

* * *

It was at a quarter to eight that the phone rang in her bedroom. She picked up the receiver, stiffening as she recognised the voice.

'So you are in—'

'Did you expect me to flout your authority and go out?' she snapped.

'Sarcasm, my child, does not become you. I wondered if you would care to join me for dinner.'

She gasped, moving the receiver to stare into it. 'Dinner?' she repeated weakly.

'Androula mentioned that you hadn't had any tea.'

She hesitated. Undoubtedly she would like to have her dinner, for by now she was hungry. But to have it with Alexis . . . Yet suddenly the prospect became pleasant, for surely he would at least assume a courteous manner with her. She heard herself say in controlled and steady tones, 'Thank you, Alexis. I will join you for dinner. What time shall I come down?'

A low laugh came over before he said, 'Precisely at a quarter past eight.'

Precisely . . . So he was being sarcastic now. Judith replaced the receiver and walked over to the mirror to take a long, measuring look at herself. Then, with a glance at her watch, she hurried to the bathroom, where she took a hasty shower.

At a quarter past eight she was standing just inside the door of the salon. Alexis was by a standard lamp and had not heard her footsteps on the soft-pile carpet. She examined his clear profile against the light, noticing the aristocratic, classical contours, the angular jaw and straight nose, the strong, determined chin. He turned; she came slowly into the room, her face aglow still from the fresh, invigorating winds which had blown down from the mountains whilst she was at the Sanctuary. The bodice of her dress fitted snugly, enhancing her curves, while the ankle-length skirt swayed attractively when she walked. Although full, it was cut so as to provide a tantalising impression of what lay beneath. For a long moment Alexis stood there, subjecting her first to a roving look, and then, as his dark eyes settled on her face, to a piercing scrutiny.

'You look charming,' was his comment at last, but there was scant expression in the words. His smile, too, was perfunctory, and for no reason she could explain, Judith felt her spirits drop.

She said flatly, 'Thank you,' and sat down, watching him as he walked with that air of superiority towards the drinks cabinet.

'What will you have?'

'A dry martini, please.'

'Ice and lemon?'

'Please.'

He gave it to her; their eyes met and held. Quivers, strangely pleasant, feathered along her back and she averted her face because she knew the colour was slowly rising in her cheeks. He stooped, and with a finger beneath her chin he forced her to look at him.

'Why did you come?' he said.

She instantly reminded him that he had already asked that question. 'I have already told you why,' she added finally.

'It was because you were dissatisfied with the work you were doing?'

'Mainly it was that. Alexis,' she said with a hint of impatience, 'can we let that drop? I definitely did not come here in order to contact you again. You could have been married for all I knew!'

'Helen would have mentioned it; you are well aware that she would.'

Judith gritted her teeth. 'All right, I give you that point. But get this! I am not here because I want to pick up any threads. What is past is past, and one should never go back.' She looked at him, dark anger in her eyes. 'In any case, you have a girl friend, and I knew you had, for Helen mentioned her in one of her letters.'

Alexis said nothing, and as she watched his face closely, trying to read what was in his eyes, she suddenly felt that he was not being pompous at all, that his question as to why she was here stemmed from another aspect altogether.

She found herself saying, in a wondering tone of voice, 'I believe you are afraid of—of finding me attractive—' She stopped, appalled at what she had said.

However, he took no objection, but actually finished for her: 'And falling in love with you all over again?' His mouth went tight. 'Yes, I am already finding you attractive, but I have no intention of falling in love with you—'

'I don't want you to!'

'I certainly would like to have an affair with you, though,' he said quietly.

She stood up, a gasp of disbelief escaping her at his audacity. 'I don't think we have anything further to say to one another. I will bid you good night.'

She moved towards the door but never reached it. With a couple of long strides he was beside her; she protested as he gripped her arm, but the next moment she was imprisoned, forced to recognise his hardness, his need of her. His mouth, brutal in its desire, crushed her lips unmercifully, while his arms about her strengthened until she felt she would never breathe again.

'I want you, Judith.' Thick his voice and insistent. 'Why hold out when your desires are equally as strong as mine?'

'They are not—!'

'My dear,' he broke in softly, 'don't lie to me; it's futile, for I know. You reciprocated beautifully before, letting me know just how much you wanted fullfilment. In Greece we *live,* Judith, live and enjoy life to the fullest. Why this pretence of coldness? Be my pillow-friend and I will give you so much—'

'Get away from me!' she cried, gasping for breath as she managed to gain her release, not by her own puny efforts, but because he allowed her to escape. She was panting, her breasts heaving, her cheeks' heightened colour betraying the strength of her emotions . . . not only anger, but passion unslaked. For there was no doubt that Alexis held her defences in the palm of his hand every time he tempted her; it had been like that during their engagement, and it was the same now. He did something to her which no other man ever could; she knew this to be an indisputable fact and admitted it. But to be his mistress—no, that was not for her! She desired him, but she did not think she loved him . . . or did she? Misery flooded over her at the possibility of yet another period of unhappiness. She had managed to get over it once. Surely she was not going to be so foolish as to fall in love again with the same man!—a man who by his own admission had no interest in marrying her, but a most strong interest in possessing her.

'Let me go,' she begged, so close to tears that her vision was misted. 'I'm tired and—'

'Have dinner with me.' His voice staggered her by its change, its gentleness and persuasiveness. 'Let us forget these past few minutes and enjoy our meal.' He touched her eye, checking a tear before it fell, and gently he touched her lips, as well, caressing them moistly, while his hand stroked her hair. 'Better now?' He smiled and she nodded, her big eyes wider than ever as they met his in bewilderment. Strange man to have these opposing facets to his nature! How must she take him?

'Yes, I feel better,' she answered in a rather shaky little voice.

'And are you hungry?' His arm was about her shoulder.

'I must admit I am,' she returned with a small laugh.

'Come, then, the dinner will be served by now.'

It was a meal eaten by candlelight, with soft music to accompany the most delicious food and wine and add to the atmosphere of romance which pervaded the room, helped by the scent of flowers, the fine china, the silver, and gleaming crystal glassware.

'Did you enjoy it?' Alexis was asking when they were back in the salon drinking coffee and cognac.

'Very much.' Her composure regained a long while ago, she was able to look directly at him, a smile on her lips. 'It was a delicious meal.'

He paused a moment before saying, his gaze steady and penetrating, 'This friend you mentioned—you've obviously met him since you arrived . . . and that isn't very long.'

'I met him on the site,' she said. 'He dropped a coin and it rolled to my feet.'

A quirk of amusement was in evidence, but only fleetingly. His voice was faintly cold as he remarked, 'Very romantic. And so you became friends on sight?'

'Not friends, exactly,' she contradicted. 'He asked me to have lunch with him and I accepted. Then we were to dine out together this evening. . . .' She allowed her voice to trail off, knowing that there was no need for further words.

'He's here on holiday?'

'That's right. He was coming with a friend, but his friend took ill, so Leslie had to come alone.'

'And he wants company . . . female company?' Terse now the tone and it brought a puzzled frown to his companion's forehead.

What was the reason for all this interest? she wondered. Jealousy? The word came naturally, the result of his saying he found her attractive. But if he were so deeply affected as to be jealous, then surely he must feel something stronger than desire for her.

'You're looking puzzled,' she heard him remark and flicked him a glance from above the
rim of her glass.

'It's your attitude, your interest in—in my affairs.'

'I'm not, really—' He lifted a hand to stifle a
yawn. 'I suppose I was merely making conversation.'

She coloured, feeling snubbed. He had a way,
this man, of making her feel small and inferior,
unable to hold her own with him. It was not a
pleasant feeling; she resented it but, reluctant to
cause dissention after such a happy evening,
she remained silent, sipping her brandy and,
inexplicably, feeling restless all at once.

As if he sensed this, Alexis said after draining
his coffee cup and placing it on the saucer,
'Would you like a stroll in the gardens? This is
the best time of the day, when the coolness
settles over everything.'

She put down her glass. To walk outside . . .
She knew the atmosphere was romantic. . . .
Refuse! said her common sense. *Accept!* said
her heart. A smile fluttered; Alexis had risen
already, as if he had no expectation of a refusal.
She took the extended hand without quite realising the intimacy of the action, and within a few
minutes they were crossing the carpet-smooth
lawn and she knew he was taking her somewhere secluded. She pulled back; he laughed
and gave her a little tug of the hand.

'Don't be scared. I'll not molest you. Haven't I
promised?'

'Yes, but . . .'

'You don't trust my word?' He had stopped
and she wanted to run.

'You've broken it already,' she reminded him. 'You promised that if I stayed you'd not—er—force your attentions on me. But you did, just a couple of hours ago.'

He looked down at her in the moonlight and gave a quirk of impatience. 'Why pretend, Judith? And why hold out against your own inclinations and desires? You haven't lived if you've never known a man's love—'

'Love?' she was swift to query.

'I didn't mean that quite literally. I meant lovemaking—the whole thing from foreplay to afterplay—'

'Please!'

'It's nature's gift,' he went on, ignoring the interruption. 'The delights of the flesh—primitive and satisfying—'

'You make it sound so clinical,' she interrupted, embarrassment forcing her to say something to put a stop to his words. 'I intend to wait for the very special man who might one day come along.'

A pause. Then, slowly, his eyes never leaving her face, 'You once thought the special man had come along.'

'You're trying to say that, to me, you ought still to be something special?' A hint of contempt edged her voice, but he seemed not to have noticed.

'What I am trying to say—or, rather, to convince you of—is that if I once was special, and taking into consideration the fact that you've never had anyone else—not anyone special, obviously—then you should feel the same about me, sexually, as you did before.'

She looked up into his face. 'You have an odd

kind of logic, Alexis,' she observed. 'But unfortunately for you it's at complete variance with mine.'

'Cool and so collected. I shall kiss you into a very different mood— No, my dear Judith, there is no escape!' He brought her protesting body to him, his arms enfolding her, pressing her so close she could scarcely breathe. His mouth, moist and warm and possessive, took hers in spite of her struggles. Her lips were coerced apart and his tongue caressed hers. She still tried to twist herself free, but his hand was low down her back, forcing her body to cease its struggles. She quivered in every cell, every nerve, while her heart raced and her pulses rioted. His other hand slid with fine expertise into her bodice to wrap itself round her breast while his fingers teased until without much effort the nipple was a hard little bud in his hand.

She managed to lift her face, to see that his eyes held the black intensity of passion. She was afraid, trembling, and yet, conversely, her body reacted to the stimulus being exerted upon it by the smooth and easy finesse of the man who seemed to have perfected the art of lovemaking. How could she fight him? If she had strength she could escape, but his arms as they slid right round her again were like bands of waxed rope, hard, inflexible. He was forcing his iron-hard frame against her suppleness, both his hands sliding down to her soft curves, fingers curling round them, masterfully insistent, demanding that she surrender her body in obedience to his. She gave way, yielding to his wishes with a sort of ecstatic languour, and the result was a momentary heady pleasure that was yet nebulous because she had no description for it. All she knew was that this was only a breath away from heaven.

'Don't you want to enjoy the full sweetness, Judith?' he whispered huskily, close to her breast. She could not answer, for an ache had caught her throat, an ache of pleasure-pain that came surging up from the depths of her heart. 'We're wasting time—and what is virginity, anyway?'

'It's something to treasure!' She felt foolish, but she had to say something. 'You shall never take it from me, so you can stop trying!'

Vehemently she spoke, but within her she harboured no illusions as to the weakness of her resistance to his charms, his profound attraction as a man. He was too masculine by far, and too versed in the art, the finesse, of making love. She felt sure he had experienced everything to the fullest, that there were no tricks—no subtle artifices or stratagems—of which he was ignorant. No, being the typical Greek, he knew it all, would have done from an early age, so unquestionably he had had plenty of practise. So what chance had she if he continued to tempt her? The trouble was she felt instantly weak and helpless when he held her, and in any fight that spelt defeat right at the start.

'You seem very sure, my child.' His voice stole into her thoughts softly and she lifted her face, a pale face, strained and frightened. 'But if you were honest, you would admit that you wouldn't stand a chance if I were to make up my mind to possess you.'

She said nothing; he was holding her, but

slackly, so she could have moved away from his embrace. But she still knew this lassitude, this drugged sensation, as if her senses were drifting away from reality. Alexis kissed her, passionately, burningly, and she reciprocated, caressing his tongue and murmuring inarticulately from the back of her throat. Pulses were beating fast in her temples, as if in competition with the racing beat of her heart.

'Your body betrays you,' he said softly, 'and you are unable to do anything about it, aren't you?'

She could not deny it, so she refrained from answering him. His mouth was moist against the pulsing hollow in her throat. His hand slid again into her dress, and this time he undid her bra before cupping her breast, kneading it gently then with feather-light fingers, teasing until the nipple again rose to the hardness of desire. He bent; she found herself unable to resist reaching up to wind her arms round his neck. A violent spasm thrilled through her whole body when he took the nipple into his mouth and touched it with his tongue. She was lost! she thought, and excitement rose to conquer the last vestige of mental resistance which she had been endeavouring to hold within her grasp.

'Let's go in,' he said hoarsely. 'I want you, Judith, and I mean to have you . . . tonight!' He gazed down into her eyes, as if challenging contradiction. She said nothing, but mentally she was aware of salvation. By the time they were in the house she would be in full control of her emotions.

Chapter Three

A week had passed since Judith's narrow escape, and she had made sure not to find herself in such a vulnerable situation again. Alexis had been frustrated when, expecting her to agree to his coming to her room, he was told rather coldly that he had been taking far too much for granted. She never had the least intention of sleeping with him.

How he had taken it was something she never found out, simply because she left him standing in the hall and ran in a somewhat undignified fashion to the security of her room, which, she had been relieved to discover, had a key in its ornate silver-gilt lock.

Judith had made Helen give her four evenings off and one full day, so she and Leslie had by now become good friends, having been together for the whole of Judith's free time. They found a cosy restaurant where it was pleasant to dine; they walked afterwards along the bank of the river, and on a couple of occasions to the shrine. Tourists rarely came after dark, so they had it to themselves, and always Judith was intoxicated by the splendour of the scene, drowsy beneath the argent light of a theatrical moon. Her senses were drugged by the flower perfumes and the peace; and the hush of night was magic in itself.

'What are you thinking?' he asked on one

occasion as they strolled along, Leslie holding her hand because, he said, she might tread on a loose stone and fall.

'As always when I come here, I think of the past glories,' she confessed a little self-deprecatingly. 'I'm a dreamer. I lose myself in imagination.'

'That is not difficult here,' he had to agree. 'I can easily see the ancients pouring into Delphi, bringing their problems, wanting prophecies, and never questioning what the Oracle told them.'

'They must have been very naïve.'

'They found it easier to believe than to argue.'

She nodded her head. She and Leslie were by the Treasury of Athens, and she could visualise all the glorious treasures which were kept inside it. And all along the Sacred Way . . . statue after statue, in gold and bronze and marble. Likenesses of athletes amongst those of the gods. Gold galore; other priceless treasures pouring into this hallowed spot, the most holy of any place in the then-known world.

'Zeus sent out two eagles—one from where the sun rose, and one from where it set. And these two eagles met at Delphi, over the navel of the earth, the *omphalos*.' Leslie stopped and smiled encouragement.

Laughing, Judith took up the story. 'Below the *omphalos* lay the sacred cave of Mother Earth's Oracle.'

'And you forgot to add that it was guarded by a hideous monster, Python.'

'I hadn't come to that yet. Apollo slew Python, and the ancients interpreted that as the victory of light over darkness.' She stopped and gazed all round, noticing how the moonlight was being diffused in silver effulgence all over the site of the sun-god's cult, and spreading in one direction to the great sea of olives, and in another to the sombre massif of Mount Parnassas, where on bright mornings eagles soared on air currents, wings gracefully spread, and motionless. 'You know, Leslie,' she said, and her voice was hushed, as if she would not wish to disturb the gods from their slumber, 'one can feel the sacredness of this place; it penetrates the mind and makes one very dubious of anything in this world actually being lost.'

He turned to stare and she saw at once that he was not quite on her wave length. And for no reason at all she wished it were Alexis who were here; he would understand, would agree with her that happenings of the past linger on in a place as sacred as this, that the gods are not dead but only resting, with their spirits free to sanctify this core of bygone holiness and purity.

'I don't quite know what you mean.' Leslie's voice came at last. Judith managed a weak smile and said it didn't matter since she could not explain, anyway. She felt instinctively that Alexis would, like her, reach out to touch the sun-heated stones carved by men of long ago, and that his sensitive fingers, like hers, would find the secrets which lay within their depths. She suddenly wanted to leave the site and go back to the villa. She mentioned her wish and, although Leslie clearly wanted her to stay a while, he agreed to take her home. They said good night at the gate; he kissed her lightly and she made no protest. Someone walked across the long drive close by the villa, and she wondered if whoever it was had seen. No matter; it would only be one of the servants, she assumed.

But it happened to be Alexis. He was standing by the fountain when she came down the drive, and she was halfway along it when she realised it was him. She would have skirted the fountain to avoid him, but he turned, knowing she was there—and no doubt knowing, too, that she was wanting to keep out of his way. She paused uncertainly, then said a hasty good night and would have moved on, but he barred her way.

'I want to talk to you, Judith.' His voice was curt, almost to the point of harshness.

'Tonight?' in some surprise. 'It's late and I'm tired. I'll see you in the morning.' She was too vulnerable out here, and she cursed herself for not realising that the shadowed figure she had seen might be that of Alexis, the last person she wanted to find herself alone with on a starlit night like this.

'It's important,' he snapped and actually gripped her wrist so she could not run from him. 'There's a seat over there—'

'I want to go in! Nothing can be so important as to require discussion at this time of night!'

Without answering, he propelled her forwards, his hand at her elbow.

'Let me go!' she cried. 'I don't know what your game is, but I am not staying out here with you, and if you don't release me I shall call for help!' She meant it, too, and he stopped, turning to her, and she saw plainly the fury on his face.

'It's about Helen, for one thing,' he said at last, and his voice had quietened.

'Helen?' What did he mean by 'for one thing'?

'She's gone—left her child.'

It was a long moment before Judith could speak, for she could scarcely take in what he had said. 'But—but she'd never leave Petros—oh, no, she couldn't! No mother would leave her child!'

'It's been done before,' he said harshly.

'She'll come back—'

'She left a note to say she was going to live with her man friend. They've already left for Athens, where he has an apartment.'

Judith shook her head, anger and disbelief mingling with the concern she felt for the little boy. 'Has she taken all her things?'

'Every stitch. I went into her room; there's not even a sign that she ever occupied it.'

Judith pulled away from his grip but stood just a few paces from him. 'All this has nothing to do with me,' she began. 'I'm still leaving at the end of the month, so—so you had better get someone for Petros. . . .' Her voice trailed off to silence. She felt callous coming out with words like those. Alexis must be almost out of his mind with worry, for it was not only that Helen had disgraced herself and all the family, but he was now faced with the task of telling everyone, and especially painful would be the telling of her husband . . . and Petros. Already he had been asking when he would be seeing his daddy again; now he would be wanting to know where his mummy had gone.

'You're not leaving, Judith.' So soft the voice, and yet imperious, commanding, inflexible.

'You'll stay indefinitely. Petros is at least used to you by now, even though you haven't been here long. I am not having him upset by producing another stranger less than two weeks from now.'

She bit her lip, having to admit that Alexis was right. For the boy's sake she would have to stay. 'I wouldn't mind staying if you'd—er . . .' Again she trailed off, painfully embarrassed because he seemed for the moment exceedingly amused. But it was a fleeting impression. When he spoke his voice again was hard.

'I promise,' was all he said, and she agreed to stay until Panos made arrangements for Petros to be looked after.

'One of his aunts might take him,' Judith suggested.

'Panos might not want to give his child to an aunt.'

Judith gave a sigh. 'I didn't ever intend to stay here indefinitely; you know that. I supposed that Helen would be going back to England as soon as Panos returned there.'

'Let us take things as they come,' he said with some asperity. 'For the time being you will stay and care for my nephew.'

'I've already said I would.' It was Judith's turn to show impatience. He did not speak, and, as the thought occurred to her, she said, 'There was something else—or so you implied.'

'Yes,' with well-studied directness. 'This young man you're meeting—I don't approve—'

'You *what*?' She quivered, glaring at him.

'You heard me,' he snapped. 'He was kissing you out there at the gate. Have you not thought what the servants will say?'

'No,' she replied tartly, 'I haven't thought! But if I had, I wouldn't have given a darn for what they might say! As for my friendship with Leslie —I shall see him on my evenings off until he leaves.'

'And when is he leaving?' There was a dangerous glint in Alexis' eyes which Judith tried to ignore.

'Not for another two weeks.' Was it imagination? she wondered. Or had Alexis actually gritted his teeth?

'You won't be able to have much time off, not now that Helen has gone.' His voice was crisp, but Judith did notice the faint lack of confidence and wondered if he had ever before doubted the strength of his own authority. 'I shall expect you to forego any further outings—' He stopped as she shook her head. 'Judith,' he said softly, 'I am asking you to do as I say.'

'You are ordering me—or trying to!' she retorted, chin in the air and cheeks aflame with anger. 'You're not in a strong enough position to give me orders, Alexis. I am not one of your weak, subservient Greek chattels whose will has been bent through centuries of time by the dominance of the male!' She was fired with resentment and little knew how her attitude had aroused his sense of humour, so that all his own anger was dissolved.

His lips were curved in a humourous half-smile and his voice quivered slightly with mirth as he said, 'Curb it, Judith, for such vehemence isn't necessary. I don't want to domineer over you—'

'Oh, yes, you do!'

'If you are not careful,' he warned with slow

deliberation, 'I shall give you a thorough shaking.'

'At your cost!'

He actually laughed, and before she had time to guess at his intent, he had placed a swift kiss on her lips.

'Perhaps,' he said with a sort of mocking amusement, 'that will put a stop to all that nonsense. And now, let us be serious. You will stay, you say?'

'Until other arrangements can be made, yes.'

'Good. And this man friend?'

'I enjoy his company.'

He gave a small sigh. 'I suppose you are right, after all,' he admitted, amazing her with his candour. 'I have no authority over your movements when you're not on duty.'

'Thank you,' she returned with an icy inflection. 'You are most accommodating.'

He drew a breath. As she looked at his changing expression, she decided that nothing would have afforded him greater satisfaction than to give her that shaking he had mentioned. But he did not dare, and the knowledge afforded her both satisfaction and enjoyment.

It was a fortnight later when Judith first met Camille. She was in the garden playing ball with Petros when the girl came swinging along after leaving her car at the forecourt in front of the villa. Judith stopped, the ball in her hand, wondering why the girl should be coming across the lawn.

'So you're the nanny my maid was telling me about,' Camille observed without preamble.

'Your maid?' with a lift of Judith's brow that

could only be described as arrogant. She took exception to the girl's manner, having guessed who she was from a description given her by Helen. Tall and fair with long, wavy hair, she was even more eye catching than Judith had visualised. Her skin was clear and tight over delicately moulded cheekbones; her mouth was wide and expertly made up. With blue eyes, widely spaced and framed by long, curling lashes, and softly sloping shoulders, Camille had the figure of a model and the confidence of a queen. Judith resented the feeling of inferiority that was creeping over her as the girl stood there, looking her over as if she were a piece of merchandise being offered for sale.

'My maid, Stella, is the sister of Androula.' She stopped, her attention having reverted to the child.

He was standing there looking awkward, and Judith, with swift perception, guessed that Petros had not taken to the girl—in fact, she was sure he actually disliked her. Had they ever met before? she wondered, and felt this was their first encounter. So she said, as much in order to break the silence than anything else, 'This is Petros, Helen's little boy.' She smiled down at him as he raised his big dark eyes. 'Say hello,' she added, broadening her smile encouragingly.

'Yassoo,' he responded in a voice so low it could scarcely be heard.

'I don't speak Greek, boy! Do you not speak English, or French?'

Petros went red and so did Judith . . . but each for a very different reason.

'You don't need to know the Greek language in order to grasp the meaning of the word he used,'

Judith said tartly. 'One only needs to be in Greece half an hour to hear it a dozen times or more.'

Arrogant, supercilious eyes rested for a long moment on Judith's flushed face. 'I think you forget your place, madam!' came the comment at last.

'My place? Who are you to speak to me like this?' Judith knew, of course, but she was forcing the girl to provide some information about herself.

'I'm Camille Longman—' The girl stopped, as if angry with herself for condescending to answer the question put to her. However, she added after a pause, 'I happen to be the future mistress of this establishment.'

'Indeed?'

Camille's blue eyes glinted like crystals of ice. 'You're very sarcastic,' she snapped. 'I shall speak to Alexis about you—*Mr. Vasilis* is how I suppose you refer to him.'

Judith's mouth curved as amusement crept into her anger, partly dissolving it. She wondered what the girl would have to say if she were to tell her the truth . . . that she had never once called Alexis by his surname.

'What is so amusing?' demanded Camille with a lift of her pointed little chin.

'As a matter of fact,' returned Judith with a hint of acid sweetness, 'you would not find it amusing at all, and therefore I shan't enlighten you.' She stopped as Petros opened his mouth to say something.

'*Piyéno.*'

Judith frowned. It was plain that the child had no intention of speaking English while Camille was here. There was something to be learnt about child psychology here, she thought, for it was obvious that this was Petros' way of showing his dislike of the girl. But of course Judith could not understand the word, either, and so she had to say, 'What does that mean, Petros?'

She was smiling encouragement and even held out her hand so he could take hold of it. He made a sign for her to bend down, which after a slight hesitation she did.

'I go, Judith—I want to go away from this nasty lady.'

Judith straightened up, her expression veiled. 'If you will excuse us,' she said politely, 'we have to go indoors.'

Camille turned without a word and strode away. Looking after her retreating figure, Judith asked herself why the girl had come over to her in the first place, and she could reach only one conclusion. Having heard of her from her maid, she wanted to take a look at the girl who was now a member of the Vasilis household.

'Can we play ball again now?' Petros was smiling as he ran away backwards, hands outstretched to catch the ball when Judith threw it.

She threw it rather harder than intended, and while Petros raced away across the lawn and into the shrubbery, she let her thoughts return to Camille. Helen had said the girl was away on holiday but was returning soon. That was the reason why she had not put in an appearance before; she must have arrived home today, or perhaps yesterday. Where did she live? Not too far away, concluded Judith. Had she any family? Was she really almost engaged to Alexis? She must be, thought Judith, or she would not have mentioned, so confidently, that she was the future mistress of this estate. For it was an estate.

In the short time Judith had been here she had explored the grounds thoroughly and was amazed at their size. The orchards of oranges, lemons, and grapefruit were vast in themselves, and there were other *perivolis*, as well, where apples, pears, and bananas grew—small bananas more delicious than any Judith had previously tasted. There were fig trees and olives, carobs and tall pines, tracts of woodland where forest trees abounded. . . . The grounds as a whole were most attractive and extensive; those close to the villa were a veritable fairyland of colour and statuary, of terraces and sunken rose beds, of rockeries and shrubberies where grew the lovely hibiscus in several delightful colours, where passionflowers opened for their brief day's glory. A hundred other exotic flowers complemented the well-manicured lawns and long, immaculately kept pathways, several of which led to little arbours or other shady little havens where one could sit and meditate undisturbed.

Yes, it was an estate, and the equally attractive low white villa was set in its midst, its aspects breathtaking in their sweep over the Sanctuary, in their long panoramic view to where the mystical Gorge of the Pleistos widened out onto the Sacred Plain of Amphissa with its numberless ancient olive trees. Mountains towered in a curve of snow-capped peaks which looked down upon the cerulean-blue of the lovely Gulf of Corinth. Above the Peloponnese Mountains, sun-brightened clouds roofed the terrain of eagles and ravens; it was a scene of untamed primordial beauty, and it required no difficult working of the mind to imagine the pagan gods abiding there, their spirits palpably alive.

'Oh, it went a long way!' Petros' strong but childish voice severed Judith's musings and she held out her hands swiftly to catch the ball, which was already on its flight.

'I think I've had enough,' she said when another five minutes had passed. 'Don't you ever get tired, Petros?'

'Only at night. I wish I had another little boy to play with—' He came up to her and reached for her hand. She closed her fingers round his and gave them an affectionate little squeeze. He was fast winning her heart and she wondered how they would both feel at the parting—when it came.

'Are there no children in the village who would come up and play with you?' she asked.

'I have some cousins, but they are bigger than me.'

'You could still play with them.' She would ask Alexis about them this evening, she decided, for she was not off duty and so would be dining with her employer—yes, that was how she now regarded Alexis, since he would be the one to be paying her a salary, unless Helen came back, of course, which seemed very unlikely.

But she did not dine with Alexis that evening. She was changed and ready and spending a few quiet moments by the window of her room when she saw Alexis and Camille leaving, in their respective cars. A weight settled, and yet she did wonder why she had taken it for granted that Camille would go home long before dinner. Judith knew she ought to have gone round to see if her car was still there, but she and Petros had entered the villa by a back door, then gone straight to the nursery. She had read a fairy story to Petros, and showed him the lovely pictures; this had brought them to teatime, after which she had given Petros his bath and put him to bed, again reading a short story to him, her soft, musical voice soon lulling him to sleep. She had sat on her verandah for a while, reading, then bathed and changed, taking time over choosing a dress and doing her hair. She had put it up for a change and felt rather pleased with the glamour it seemed to give her. That she was competing with Camille never entered her head, and if she *was* competing it was entirely an unconscious act. Whichever way, she had wasted her time.

Disconsolate, she took off her dress, let down her hair, and got into a pair of cotton jeans and put a short-sleeved shirt-blouse over it. She felt listless and unsettled, could not decide whether to send down for a tray or not. She put a finger on the bell, then withdrew it again. Somehow she felt she could not eat alone; perhaps it was an uneasy reaction, a sort of anticlimactic result of looking forward to dining by candlelight with Alexis. Yes, she was admitting that she had looked forward to it in spite of the trickle of coolness which seemed always to intrude into their relationship these days.

Automatically she found herself going into Petros' bedroom. He was sound asleep, peacefully relaxed as only the young can be. He would not waken. . . .

The idea came and was dismissed. This was

not one of her evenings off. And yet . . . Androula was there, and Lefki, the girl who worked in the kitchen most of the time, helping the cook. Yes, there was Eva, too, plump and homely and always doting on the little boy, who was now without both mother and father. She suspected the truth, thought Judith, although she did not think that Eva had passed on her suspicions to any of the other servants, who had been told by Alexis that his sister had gone on a visit to some friends in Athens.

Judith swallowed saliva collecting in her mouth; she never did like indecision, for she had a tidy mind normally. Yet the restlessness persisted; she looked at her watch to find that it was not quite eight o'clock. With sudden resolve she went back to her own room and picked up the receiver. Leslie, with only a few more days of his holiday left, was overjoyed at the prospect of her joining him for dinner.

'I was intending to have it here, in my room,' he said. 'But now we can go out! We can dine at the Apollon Hotel; I'm told it's well known for its specialties in Greek food.'

'Where shall we meet?'

'I've still got the hired car, so I'll come for you.'

'I'll be at the gate.'

'It'll not take me more than five minutes.'

'What's the place like? I mean, would one need to dress up?' She did not feel like changing again.

'Not at all. No one ever bothers these days, anyway. Besides, you always look as if you've stepped right out of a bandbox!'

The line went dead before Judith could say

anything to that. She replaced the receiver with shaking fingers, stood a moment to calm herself, then went down to the kitchen and through it to the sitting-room provided for the staff. Four people were watching the television—three women and one of the gardeners. She said she was going out and asked that they go up to Petros regularly throughout the evening. She was giving her own work to someone else and suddenly she hesitated, about to say it did not matter, as she had changed her mind. But what about Leslie's disappointment when she met him at the gate and said she was not going, after all? Torn once more by indecision, she looked from one to the other. The three women spoke at once, in varying degrees of broken English.

'Certainly, Miss.'

'It no trouble at all,' from Androula, who was always ready to oblige, no matter what was asked of her.

'Do not worry, *kyria!* Little Petros will be well looked after!'

'Thank you, Eva.' Judith was reassured; she proceeded to the gate with a light step and a few minutes later was in the car, relaxed against the upholstery.

'How is it that you managed to get away?' Leslie wanted to know as soon as they were on their way.

'I oughtn't to be here. I felt restless, though, and as there are three women in the house to look after Petros, I decided to phone you and see if you wanted me to join you for dinner.'

'*If* I wanted to! Judith, you knew darned well that I'd be delighted!' Eager and youthful, thought Judith. So very different from Alexis with his quiet dignity and high-bred look.

'It's nice to be wanted,' she said, speaking her thoughts aloud, then switching mentally to a picture of Alexis dining with Camille. He wanted her, evidently . . . but he did not want Judith, for otherwise he would have dined at home, knowing it was her night on duty and that she would be alone. But why should he want her? Why should he care if she was alone? After all, she was only the nanny to his nephew and she would be gone just as soon as Alexis notified Panos of what had happened and Panos came hurrying home to make provisions for his son to be looked after. As yet Alexis had not told his mother, or any of the family, about Helen's departure. Yet he could not keep quiet much longer.

Leslie was driving slowly, taking the bends with rather more care than she would have expected.

'Judith,' he said, breaking into the silence that had settled between them, 'I want you to promise we'll keep in touch. You said you'd not be here much longer, and once you're back in England we can see each other, can't we?'

'I don't know, Leslie.' She sighed. He was far too young for her, and in any case, although she liked him enormously and enjoyed going about with him, she felt nothing stronger than friendship, comradeship, and she knew there would never be anything deeper on her part. She had no wish that he should fall in love with her and get hurt. 'To tell the truth, I don't really know how long I shall be here. I didn't tell you, but Petros' mother has gone off, deserted him, and so I must stay until his father comes home and makes arrangements for him.'

'His mother's gone?' Leslie's voice was edged with disbelief. 'But why? I mean, where has she gone, and why? When we first met, you said she was here only because her husband was away in Portugal and she hadn't wanted to go with him, preferring to come home to her native land for a while.' Leslie turned into the hotel entrance as he spoke and the car was slowing down. Lights flared and *bouzouki* music could be heard. Noise. The Greeks loved it! No music should carry this far, she mused.

'Helen has found someone else.' She spoke abruptly, not wanting further questions and already regretting her confidence.

'Someone else! But Greek wives never do!'

Judith had to smile. 'Why should they be any different? Marriages are always breaking up everywhere. It makes you scared, wondering if your own will end up the same way.'

She guessed he was frowning as he got out of the car. He came round before she could manipulate the door handle and opened it for her.

'It certainly pays us to make sure before we even think of marriage. If you and I—'

'It looks as if they're very busy.' The interruption was deliberate. Leslie took the hint and dropped the subject altogether. They were fortunate in getting a table just vacated. It was in a secluded corner by an open window and the breeze came in gently, on fairy wings, its presence welcome, for the room was filled to capacity. On a dais four musicians were playing while two men danced on a glass circle on the floor just to one side of them. They were performing the Zorba *syrtaki*, having been joined swiftly by several other men in black turtleneck sweaters. There was noise from chattering groups at tables and from a large gathering that was clustered at the door, hopefully waiting to get a table. But they were turned away, much to Judith's relief. It lessened the noise a little.

'What are you having?' Leslie had been perusing the menu, but Judith's eyes were on the dancers. She loved to see the suppleness, the expert gyrations and leaping of the men, their agility being sometimes quite unbelievable since they seemed often to be middle-aged.

But she brought her attention to the menu, choosing as a starter the favourite Greek soup, *avgolémono*, made with eggs, lemon juice, rice, and a rich stock. To follow she wanted the delicious fish *plaki*. Leslie ordered the soup, then chicken in wine for the main course. He ordered a bottle of local wine which came in a cooler which was placed beside their table.

For dessert they both had fresh fruit and finished with coffee and liqueurs.

Leslie had done most of the talking during the meal. When they had finished and a small dish of sweetmeats was placed on the table, he said with an odd inflection, 'You've been very quiet tonight, Judith. Is something wrong?'

She managed a faint smile. 'I suppose I'm feeling guilty. I oughtn't to be here at all.'

'Good God!' He frowned. 'That fellow's not a schoolmaster that you should be feeling you're playing truant and are to be punished for it!'

He actually glowered at her across the table and she did not know whether to be amused— because this manner did not suit his lack of

73

maturity at all—or to be angry that he should take the liberty of speaking to her like this. She managed to control both emotions, her voice lacking expression as she answered quietly, 'I *am* playing truant, Leslie.'

He drew a breath and his mouth went tight. 'He's not even your employer!'

'He is now that Helen has gone.'

'You ought not to be there, Judith.' He looked pleadingly at her, all his anger and indignation gone. 'I wish you'd consider coming back home soon.'

'It's impossible. I can't leave little Petros until his father makes arrangements for his welfare.'

'When is his father coming home?'

'He'll obviously return as soon as possible. His home's in England, as I mentioned, and he might decide to take Petros over there and find a nanny for him.'

Leslie looked at her and she knew what was in his mind before he spoke. 'He'll obviously ask you to be nanny—if he does decide to bring the child to his home in England. It will mean that you and I can meet because you'll not be too far away. Berkshire, I think you once mentioned?'

She nodded her head. 'I might not want to remain in this kind of post.' She was wondering how she could convey her sentiments without hurting him. 'On the other hand, Panos might decide to leave Petros here for the time being. There are several aunts who, I am sure, would love to have him, for he's a most attractive and obedient child. He has a charming personality.'

'If his father does make that decision, then you'll be coming back to England, anyway.'

'Yes,' she agreed with a sigh.

'What's the matter, Judith?' he asked persuasively. 'You like me a little, surely?'

'I like you—' She managed a smile. 'But, Leslie, there is nothing else I feel for you.'

'Not yet, perhaps, but we get along so well. . . .' His voice trailed off as she shook her head, not a negative gesture, but one merely designed to make him drop the subject. He looked deflated but went on perseveringly: 'Judith, I have never liked a girl as much as I like you. It could soon be something deeper, believe me!'

That was what she had been afraid of. 'It takes two,' she reminded him gently. 'At present, Leslie, I'm not ready to settle down with one particular man.' Her thoughts fled swiftly to her employer and another sigh escaped her. She did wish that Alexis' face would not intrude so. Lately it seemed to be always before her.

'You're twenty-six—it's the time when most girls would be wondering if they're doomed to spinsterhood.'

Judith had to smile. Had he stopped to think before saying a thing like that? It was another sign of his immaturity.

'I'm not particularly afraid of being on my own,' she assured him presently. And then she added, still in the same gentle tone, 'You are only twenty-three, and the man should be older, if only by a couple of years or so.'

'You are saying I'm too young for you?' Indignation edged his voice.

'Yes, as a matter of fact, I am,' she answered decisively, admitting at last that there was no simple, painless way of enlightening him as to the futility of his efforts. 'I'm the sort of woman

who prefers an older man as my husband.'
Again Alexis' face intruded—his maturity, his
outstanding perfection as a man. She looked at
her companion contemplatively and decided he
would make a good, kind husband to someone,
but never could he be as exciting as Alexis.
Exciting . . . Was that all she desired—to be ex-
cited? No, she wanted more than that; she wanted something spiritual in her marriage, which
could never be possible with Alexis, who, being
a Greek, considered nothing quite so important
as the physical side of marriage.

'You're telling me there's no hope?' The pleading quality was still there, even though Leslie
had sagged in his chair as if resigned.

'I'm sorry,' she said. 'You'll find someone nice
one day, Leslie—'

'I've found someone nice!'

'I think we must be going,' she said, ignoring
the vehement declaration. 'I don't want to be too
late.'

'Very well.'

He was quiet as they left the hotel and crossed
the well-lit open space where the car was parked
beneath the trees. The night was balmy, with
stars in glittering pageantry above the drowsy
land. She caught the waft of wild jasmine fes-
tooning the bowed branches of a tree, admired
its virginal white blossoms and likened their
perfume to a nostalgic memory. She remembered that wild jasmine grew in Alexis' garden
. . . and she had smelt its fragrance one night
when she and he were talking out there. Alexis
. . . always Alexis . . . Undoubtedly he was having a most profound effect on her, causing this
restlessness, this vague sensation of having lost

something precious long ago when they quarrelled. He had demanded that she apologise, and she had in her anger taken that as uncalled-for arrogance and domination . . . but now . . . Perhaps because she was older she could see his point of view, could agree that she ought not to have gone out with another man when she was engaged to Alexis, harmless as her action was in her own eyes. Greeks were possessive where their womenfolk were concerned, and she had in fact resigned herself to having to conform, as she had confessed to Helen.

Well, what was done was done and it was far too late for self-recrimination now, when Alexis had found someone else.

'Can I take you for a little run?' Leslie interrupted her thoughts and she turned her head. They had reached the car and he was by the door. 'Just a short drive?'

'It's late—'

'No, it isn't, Judith. It's not yet ten o'clock.'

She hesitated, feeling sorry for him, but at the same time anxious to get back. In the end she agreed to let him drive her for a quarter of an hour and no more. He paused, frowning.

'It's not worth bothering about,' he complained. 'Make it half an hour.'

'All right,' she agreed resignedly, hoping Alexis would not be home before her. She did not need to worry, she assured herself. Alexis was with Camille, so it was most unlikely that he would be home much before midnight.

The car windows were open and Judith savoured the fresh breeze drifting into the car. She leant back, determined to relax and enjoy the ride. Leslie chatted, which took her mind off the initial anxiety she had felt at being out, and she soon was able to look round and appreciate the beauty of the night. The mountains rose darkly against the star-spangled back cloth of a Grecian sky; the foothills were not so sombre, though, for lights twinkled from the windows of peasants' villas and from the inevitable *kentrons* and *cafeneions* which were always scattered about the villages and their outskirts. The tall campanile of a church shone brightly in the headlights' glare, and away down over that sea of dark olives the lights of a ship could be discerned on the horizon. She was about to comment on it when the car swerved and she found herself clinging to the door.

'What—?' She got no further, for the car, out of control, hurtled down a bank at the side of the road, smashed into a huge boulder, and came to a grinding halt.

'God! That was a close thing!' Leslie, as shaken as Judith, opened his door but then turned to her. 'Are you all right?'

'I'm not hurt, if that's what you mean.' But she was trembling all over, and when she alighted from the car her legs almost gave way beneath her. 'What happened? Was it the steering?'

There was a strange hesitation before he answered, 'I could lie and say yes—but it wasn't the steering.'

'Then . . . ?' She stared in the darkness, bewilderment in her eyes.

'I lost my concentration,' he confessed in a low and self-accusing tone. 'I was—thinking, about us.'

She drew an impatient breath. This disaster

proved more than ever just how immature he was!

'What are we to do now?' she wanted to know, naturally filled with anxiety about getting back to the villa. 'We must be miles from any habitation.' She did not mention anything about getting the car on the road again simply because she saw at once that it was an impossibility without some mechanical help.

'There isn't anything to do but start walking and hope we get a lift.' He sounded bleak and contrite as he added, 'I'm so sorry, Judith. I ought to have had more sense than to lose my concentration on a road like this.'

Or any road, she almost said but refrained. Leslie was upset enough already without her making things worse for him.

They began to walk, and it seemed as if everything was against them, for the sky became overcast so that stars and moon were blotted out. Leslie began to talk, but for Judith conversation was an ordeal with her anxiety pressing so heavily on her mind. If Alexis should arrive home before her . . . She shuddered as an icy-cold blast seemed to whip itself round her.

'I wish someone would come along,' she was saying twenty minutes after the accident. 'It's incredible that no one's on the road.'

'This road isn't used much,' he told her. 'After all, it's a mountain road and people tend to avoid it as much as possible, even in daylight.'

She wanted to ask why he had chosen such a lonely road but again desisted. There was nothing to be gained by complaining.

It was another quarter of an hour before a car came along. Leslie stepped out a little way into the road and lifted his arms urgently. The driver put a finger on the horn and Leslie hurriedly stepped back.

'Scared,' he said briefly. 'Can't blame anyone for not wanting to give lifts these days.'

However, when another car came along the sudden crunching of tires on the rough surface of the road gave evidence that its driver had not the same fear as the previous one. But as she recognised the car, Judith gave a gasp of disbelief and her lips formed the silent word: *Alexis*. Of all the people it could have been, it had to be him! The shock wave of apprehension left her legs so weak they could scarcely support her. Alexis slid out, as supple and graceful as the most lithe jungle cat. Judith's heart gave a great lurch and then seemed to bump back into place abruptly, as if netted by a stranglehold similar to that which gripped her legs, depriving them of strength. As always, fear bred anger; she had never been able to separate the two and she often wondered if, should she be faced with an attacker, she would kill him if she could, driven by the wild abandon of her fury.

'You . . . !' She heard him ejaculate before his eyes began to smoulder as he realised she was with a man. 'What the—!'

'I've had an accident,' interrupted Leslie, taking a step forwards automatically. 'If you would oblige us by taking us back to the village?' He stopped somewhat abruptly as Judith touched the sleeve of his jacket.

'This is Mr. Vasilis, my—employer,' she stammered through the constriction of her throat. 'Mr.—I mean—Alexis, this is the friend I mentioned, Leslie Brockhurst.'

Leslie extended a hand in the darkness, but it was ignored, a circumstance which only served to increase Judith's anger.

'So you want a lift,' said Alexis between his teeth. 'Get in!'

'I say,' began Leslie, abashed, 'I'm terribly sorry for all this trouble. It wasn't any fault of Judith's—I mean, the accident. I took my attention from the road—'

'Get in,' repeated Alexis curtly. And he slid into the driver's seat and switched on the engine.

'You ought to tell him where he gets off!' snapped Leslie as he sat close beside Judith in the back of the car. 'What right—'

'Shh!' she broke in urgently. 'He'll hear you!'

'I was whispering.' A sulky note now and Judith sighed impatiently.

'It's best if you just say nothing,' she advised. 'Alexis in a temper is someone not to be crossed.'

Leslie set his mouth and leant back.

'If you would stop at the Artemis Hotel,' she said, pressing forwards in her seat, 'Leslie's staying there.'

No answer, but a quarter of an hour later the car pulled up on the hotel's forecourt and Leslie got out. He hesitated and would have begun an explanation of some kind, but Judith gave no opportunity for him to do so as she said, 'Good night, Leslie. I'll give you a ring in the morning about nine o'clock.'

He hesitated again, but on noting Judith's expression he returned her 'good night' and walked away. The car shot forwards with an unnecessary jerk which sent Judith back sharply against the seat. She was on the opposite side of Alexis and could just discern something of his profile in the gloom of the car: set, like the inert line of some Greek statue—the same straight classical nose and thrust-out jaw, the forceful chin, clear-cut and rigidly threatening. Was there to be a scene once they were back in the villa? What would he say to her—? More frightening—what would he *do*? Well, she decided philosophically, he could scarcely murder her, or even inflict any really painful bodily harm. Suddenly she was aware of a fatalistic sensation, heavily oppressive, but not enough to crush her altogether. She would fight him if he tried to force his attentions on her . . . for that was the only thing she could suppose he would do in his anger against her. She heard his voice at last, harsh, clipped, and demandingly imperious. Enough in itself to make her bristle!

'What explanation have you for your behaviour tonight?' She could not reply because of the choking sensation that seemed to be drying out her mouth and tongue. 'You've left Petros, neglected your duty! Have you nothing to say?'

'Would it do any good?' managed Judith at length. 'All I will tell you is that I felt lonely and decided to do something about it. Petros is all right; there are plenty of people in the house—'

'That's no excuse for neglecting your duty!' He had brought the car to a standstill with a grinding of the brakes and he had flung open his door. Judith got out and moved swiftly up the steps, preceding him, but it was not long before he stood at her side.

She had rung the bell and the door was opened

by Eva, who, all smiles, instantly said, almost as if she knew by instinct that there was tension in the atmosphere, '*Kalispera!* Little Petros has not wakened for one single moment!' She stood aside.

Judith, in her gratification, could not resist the upwards sweep of her lashes which clearly said, *I told you he would be all right.*

Nevertheless, that did not let her off the trouncing she had at first expected. Her colour became more pronounced as Alexis went on to admonish her, and although she made one or two attempts to retaliate, his arrogant, dictatorial attitude was so disturbing that her own indignant words faltered to a stop beneath the strength of his. He was in an explosive mood and she half-suspected that the responsibility thrust upon him when his sister left her child had more than a little to do with how he was feeling.

'You'll stay in each evening when you're on duty!' he gritted, his dark eyes rivetted gloweringly on her flushed face. 'Do you understand me?'

Judith's temper flared. It was her turn to glower, for of all the things he had said to her, this last sentence riled her the most.

'I'm not an imbecile!' she flashed at him from the distance she had strategically put between them when they entered the sitting-room. The drapes were still open so that the scene outside was faintly visible—the dark and mellowed outline of the buildings on the Sanctuary, the sombre mountains with their heads veiled in ominous clouds, the twinkling lights upon the hillsides, given out from the neat little villas nestling there. So peaceful! Yet here, in this lovely room, only anger and dissention—two people who had once planned to marry, quarrelling and glaring at each other as if only bitter hatred existed between them now. Judith's heart caught and she was way back in the past, when she had been so much in love with him that, had he insisted, she would most likely have given herself before marriage.

Unwanted tears filled her eyes and she had to flick them away, thus revealing to Alexis that which she so desperately wanted to hide: her own unhappiness at this enmity between them. He stared and frowned, then drew a breath which might have stemmed from impatience or anger, or something unknown to Judith, for at this moment his expression was unfathomable. So tall he stood, his figure dominating the room as it invariably did. So immaculate, with a snow-white shirt beneath the expensively cut beige linen suit, its blouson jacket fitting loosely for casual elegance combined with comfort.

'I'm going to bed,' she uttered in desperate haste as Alexis took a step in her direction.

'Not yet,' softly and with another step forwards. 'I haven't finished with you, my girl.' A small pause and then, his eyes fixing hers in a deep scrutiny: 'Why are you crying?'

'Crying?' with feigned surprise which was totally wasted, as she saw by the hint of amusement that entered his eyes. 'I'm not crying. Do you think so much of yourself—and your bullying—that you can make me cry?' With a toss of her lovely head she turned to take hold of the door handle. 'Good night, Alexis.'

Somehow, she had not had much confidence

in making such an easy escape as she was attempting. With a couple of silent strides Alexis was at her side and she felt his hard grip on her wrist, a grip which, accompanied by an unceremonious jerk, brought her slender body round to face his.

'You're not going to bed yet.' His eyes were intent as they looked into hers, their expression of quiet concern appearing totally out of place with the implacable words he uttered next. 'I haven't finished with you yet. I want to know why you're crying, and I also want to know what's between you and the man you were with. You are not leaving this room until I have an answer to both questions.' His grip tightened so that she bit her lip against the pain. 'Well?' No answer from Judith, and he added tersely, 'You've just called me a bully. You might have effective evidence of that if you don't answer me,' he said in a dangerously soft but warning voice. Judith eyed the door, estimating her chances of escape should she manage to free herself from the vicious grip of his long brown fingers round her wrist. Hoping to take him by surprise, she wrenched suddenly, even though the pain made her wince. She was free and tugging at the door handle. . . .

'Never underestimate me,' he was saying about one minute after having bruised her lips and crushed the breath right out of her. His dark, handsome face was close to hers as he added, his warm breath fanning her trembling lips, 'You've asked for it this time, so don't give me any reminders of a promise I made—'

'I did not ask for it!' She seethed, trying to

free a hand to use with violence on his cheek. 'Why must you always be wanting to use your brute strength against me?'

He gave a low laugh and answered, 'You know why. I want you, Judith—want your body, your softness in yielding surrender as once it was— remember?' The strong masculine voice was reduced to a mere caress and the movement of his body was an almost tender invitation. She felt again the fresh clean breath on her face, and in her sensitive nostrils the nostalgic male smell of him . . . like a memory which for so long has been elusive but now recaptured. . . . Heady with emotions born of recollections, swept along by visions of beauty that were also surrender, driven by the betrayal of her own desires, Judith had no armour with which to combat the accumulation of forces building up against her, and with a little moan of resignation she relaxed her body against him, and she lifted her face to offer her quivering lips to his. The low laugh again, this time the ring of triumph in its depths.

'At last you're giving in?' Half-question and half-statement. Judith stirred as if she would stage one last scene of battle, but Alexis, eyes narrowed perceptively, was swift to take her lips, forcing them apart so that his tongue could caress hers, its roughness an erotic aid to his victory and her complete surrender. She quivered when his warm, sensuous fingers touched her breast, lightly, temptingly, before they took the nipple, bringing it with slow deliberation to a hard little point which he took between his lips. More than ever the heady male aroma of him helped sensitize her erotic desires; her response to the rhythm of his hard, muscular body became wildly out of control as wave after wave of torrid passion flowed through every cell in her body. Molten lava spread relentlessly along her nerve-ends; she clung to him, little moans of rapture escaping from the parched reluctance of her throat. 'You're lost, Judith. . . .' The hoarse whisper was confident and triumphant beneath the vibrance of its passion. 'You'll be my pillow-friend?'

She quivered from head to foot, vitally aware that she was about to make a decision that would alter her whole life. If she refused him she would be forever cast out of his life; if she surrendered he would never marry her, because Greeks never ever married a pillow-friend.

'Alexis, I—'

'Don't falter,' he broke in with a mastery that frightened even while it thrilled. 'You want me just as strongly as I want you. Live, child—live!'

Chapter Four

Judith stood on the patio watching the two children playing on the lawn and a deep sigh escaped her. If only she could go back to childhood, where there were no complications in her life, where decisions didn't have to be made . . . where people were kind to you, and understanding of things like the inability to make up one's mind about something.

She turned slowly, to face the man who, these days, was rarely out of her thoughts.

His eyes were hard, his voice even harder when he spoke. 'Panos will be here the day after tomorrow.'

'I see. . . .' She looked into his eyes and fought back the tears which threatened her own. 'He will make provisions for his son?' Her brooding eyes swept towards the lawn again. She had become more and more attached to the little boy, and he to her. If only Alexis were different, not so demanding and inflexible, then she would consider staying, if that was what Panos wanted, of course. Perhaps he would in fact invite her to go with him to England. She thought she would accept, for apart from her affection for Petros, she knew she could be very content in that stately home in Berkshire, one of Britain's loveliest counties. Content . . . but not happy. Never, she thought with a pessimism unfamiliar to her, would she be happy again.

Perhaps, after all, she should have given in to Alexis. . . .

How close she had come! Memory brought the blood coursing into her cheeks as she saw again that bedroom: she and Alexis undressing . . . she and Alexis naked and ready to get onto the bed. . . . And then quite suddenly it all seemed so sordid in her eyes. Two people, mating without love, mating like animals with one fiery thought in mind—that of assuaging the desperate craving of the flesh. She had fought him like a wildcat from the raw jungle, fought with the only weapons given her by nature, her fingernails . . . and she had left marks to match the ugly bruises she herself had come by in a conflict which in the end she had lost. Only her desperate pleading, and the flood of tears, had at last seemed to move him—or perhaps he had decided that to take her by force was not going to be satisfying, after all. Whatever his reason, Alexis had picked up her dress, flung it into her face, and, picking up the dressing-gown he had thought to bring along, he had swung it round him and left the room.

Looking back now, she wondered if she would have felt differently had they decided to go to her room, or even to his. But Alexis had suggested a small bedroom tucked away at one end of the house. None of the servants would be likely to pass nearby, he had said, and so they would be safer there.

She heard Alexis' voice breaking into her reverie. 'Why the blushes? It's all over and done with!'

She nodded dumbly. Did he know she was still in love with him? Still . . . ? She rather thought that her initial love had almost died during the years of separation, and that if she had not been so foolish as to come here, knowing she would meet him again, she might now be happy. Instead, she had this weight to bear, and all because she had been so confident that she had become immune to the attractions of the man to whom she had once been engaged.

'Yes,' she agreed flatly when he seemed to be expecting some sort of response from her. 'It's all over and done with.'

'You're your own worst enemy,' he asserted. 'You've made yourself unhappy— No, don't deny it!' he said with a swift, imperious flick of the hand when she would have interrupted. 'Your eyes betray you—as they always have and always will.'

She lowered them beneath a gaze that was plainly contemptuous. 'One day,' she murmured almost against her will, 'you'll want to marry; you'll realise that all this playing round isn't leading you anywhere.'

He shrugged his broad shoulders. 'You're probably right.' He paused in thought for a space. 'I did once contemplate marriage, didn't I?' She made no answer, and he went on presently: 'Wives can be so damned wearing. They always want to improve you. They have this insatiable— and perplexing—desire for a model of perfection which they can proudly show off to their envious friends. 'Aren't I clever?' is their attitude. 'My particular catch is unique!'

She looked up, eyes brighter than she would have wanted them to be. But her voice was faintly scornful as she said, 'You obviously consider yourself to be one of these unique catches. Have you considered just how pompous that sounds?'

'I haven't been caught,' he reminded her, bypassing her question. 'It is because I have no intention of being moulded that I keep clear of marriage.'

Judith had to smile despite the way she was feeling, although the smile was a weak little attempt. 'I cannot see you allowing any woman to mould you, as you put it.' He did not speak, and she added with a curious inflection, 'You weren't bothered about *my* trying to mould you. After all, Alexis, as you yourself have just mentioned—you did once contemplate marriage.'

He looked hard at her, the most odd expression on his face. If only she could know what went on in that arrogant head of his!

'I expect I'd have regretted the impulse long ago—'

'That's about the most rotten thing you've said to me yet!' Judith's explosive accusation came of its own volition, and her colour swiftly heightened again at the sudden lift of his brows.

'I don't think I understand. Hasn't the present situation proved that marriage between us would have turned out to be a failure?'

She stared at him, again wishing she could read his mind. For it seemed as if he were challenging her . . . and also as if he were trying to convince himself of the truth of his words.

Judith found herself saying, slowly and deliberately, 'Somehow, Alexis, I can't see you admitting to failure—in anything.'

He seemed to give a start; but if he had been taken aback, then he very quickly recovered, his voice taking on a casual ring as he replied, 'We all fail sometime in our lives. I'm sure you'll agree that none of us is infallible.'

'So what you're really saying is that I, too, would now be regretting our marriage?'

He nodded, but slowly, and only after a slight hesitation which Judith was quick to notice.

'Marriage is something you have to work at,' said Judith in order to end the long silence which was spreading between them. 'To admit failure is a weakness which I firmly believe neither one of us possesses. . . .' What was she trying to do? Win him over? Convince him that marriage to her would be one big success? Embarrassed by these thoughts, she averted her face, then turned from him altogether, her attention once again directed at the two children playing ball on the lawn. 'It's nice for Petros to have a playmate. How long is Andreas staying?'

'About a week.' Andreas was one of Petros' cousins, and it was owing to Judith's persuasion that Alexis had asked that he stay at the villa for a while. Alexis had at last told the family of Helen's act in going off and living in Athens with another man. His mother, he told Judith, was taking it very badly, indeed. She was old-fashioned; her generation would always be shocked by scandal of this kind. 'Petros needs someone of his own age. Andreas beats him every time with that ball. Watch them.'

'I have been. Petros doesn't mind; he's so happy to have someone, and Andreas is very good with him.' At that moment eight-year-old

Andreas looked in their direction and then came running up.

'Uncle Alexis—can we have a tent outside tonight? We want to camp out.'

Watching him, Judith caught her breath at Alexis' expression. It was suddenly free from all harshness, all arrogance. His voice matched as he said almost gently, a hand coming out to stroke the boy's dark, curly hair. 'I don't think it would be a good idea, Andreas. I have a feeling we shall be in for a storm. You'd not like to be out there when it's thundering and lightning, would you?'

The boy looked up at the sky. 'I don't like the thunder,' he said.

'In which case you and Petros will be happier in your own little beds.'

Andreas hesitated and then, with a small sigh of resignation, 'Yes, I suppose so.' He said something in Greek and then ran off to join Petros.

'He was asking where his Aunt Helen is.' Alexis' voice was like a rasp. 'She has much to answer for, that sister of mine!'

'She must have been unhappy with Panos.' Judith was not making excuses for Helen, but merely voicing an opinion.

Alexis shot her a darkling glance. 'You agree with her action?' His mouth went tight. 'There is *no* excuse for a mother to desert her child!'

'I know—I agree. If my marriage broke up, I'd take the child with me. . . .' Her voice trailed off to silence as she saw Alexis' expression.

'You're so sure your husband would let you take his child?'

Judith drew a breath of asperity. 'I don't intend to start another argument,' she told him shortly. 'You and I will never agree on anything as far as I can see!'

'How right you are!' he snapped. Then to her amazement he laughed. 'We've certainly agreed on *that*,' he said, and Judith found herself catching his humour. Alexis watched the smile come to her lips, the gleam of amusement to her eyes, and for a long moment the atmosphere between them was tense, vaguely emotional, and each knew that the other would not speak to bring the strange silence to an end. At last Alexis turned and left her standing there, her eyes following his tall figure until it had disappeared through the door of the room behind the patio. An ironic smile replaced the one Alexis had seen. It was bordering on the farcical, she mused, that the only thing she and Alexis had agreed on was her assertion that they would never agree on anything!

Panos, his swarthy face drawn, his hands clenched tightly at his sides, paced the room for a few moments before, aware of the frowning expression of his brother-in-law, he sat down with his back to the window. Judith had been called into the room a few minutes after Panos arrived at the villa, having come by taxi from Athens. He and Alexis had had a mere few minutes together before Androula came out to the garden, where Judith was reading to the two little boys, and told her she was wanted inside the house. Judith entered the salon to find Panos pacing the floor, and although she felt sorry for him, she also felt sorry, in a way, for the wife who had deserted him. For not by any stretch of the imagination could Panos be described as attractive. But it was not just his looks and the stocky figure which contrasted so noticeably with that of Alexis. No, it was something from within the man—his character, which had never appealed very much at all to Judith. As Helen said, he was bossy, dictatorial. But so was Alexis dictatorial, mused Judith as her eyes passed from one to the other as she stood there, just inside the door after obeying the summons sent to her a moment ago. Yes, Alexis was also dictatorial . . . yet there was a subtle difference in the way he carried it off. Panos was somehow uncouth, even though he could be described as a gentleman. Now, as he sat down on the chair, his face wore an expression of injured innocence which caused Judith to draw a breath of impatience. Now was not the occasion for self-pity. It was the time to think of the more important and pressing matter of his little son's immediate future.

'Panos wants to speak to you,' said Alexis curtly. He glanced at his brother-in-law. 'I'll leave you—'

'No—stay!' Panos turned to Judith. 'Did you know my wife had this lover?' he demanded.

'Certainly not!' Indignation was stemmed, but with difficulty. Judith did not want to jeopardise her charge's happiness by being dismissed on the spot, a circumstance she could very well visualise happening, with Panos in a mood like this. He was scowling at her, dark eyes intense with wrath.

'She must have told you something!'

'I was not in Helen's confidence,' returned

Judith quietly, and as she caught Alexis' eye she felt sure he was approving the way she was dealing with this situation.

'She must have had this man a long time!'

'Perhaps. I would not know.'

Panos continued to glower at her. 'She *must* have mentioned this lover to you before she went away!'

Judith glanced again at Alexis. He said with a sort of quiet impatience, 'Exactly what are you getting at, Panos?'

'I think that Judith could have warned me!'

'Warned you?' Judith blinked. 'I didn't even know where you were.'

'Nor did Judith know of this other man—at least, not until almost the last moment before Helen went off. Look, Panos, unfortunate as the whole miserable business is, this sort of brooding cross-examination of someone not concerned with the private affairs of you and your wife is getting you nowhere. It is Petros you should be thinking of. He's without a mother. What provisions are you intending to make for him?'

'Helen—if she hadn't gone—'

'Helen *has* gone!' broke in Alexis exasperatedly. 'She—isn't—here—Panos,' he added, with deliberate emphasis on every word. 'You as Petros' father now have the responsibility of looking after him. He needs a nanny. Have you anyone in mind?'

'How can I have . . . ?' His voice faded as he looked at Judith. 'You—will you stay?'

'I shall have to think about it,' she answered, her eyes seeing the lovely English country mansion set amidst green gardens, with woodlands beyond. 'I'm returning to England soon, so I—'

'To England?' cut in Panos almost angrily. 'Then you cannot look after my Petros, can you?'

'But . . .' She stopped on catching Alexis' expression, the most incredible idea having entered her mind. 'I took it for granted,' she murmured, still watching Alexis closely, 'that you would be taking Petros back to his home in England.'

'I have to stay for one year in Portugal.'

'I could still be in your employ—in England.'

'Petros would be better off staying here.'

Silence. Alexis moved over to one of the side windows and stood looking out, hands thrust deeply into his pockets. Judith sighed, silently but long. She looked at Panos, stared over his shoulder to take in the same—or almost the same—view as that upon which Alexis was gazing: the massif of the mighty Phaedriades—the Shining Ones, as named by the ancients—their peaks indistinct amongst the clouds, forming a dramatically harsh back cloth to the screenplay spectacle of the sacred ruins; the great 'sea of olives'—silver and green against the azure endlessness of the sky; the distant and beautiful Gulf of Corinth, with its aquamarine waters spreading to the far horizon, where two ships seemed to be motionless and so tiny from this distance. Much closer were the gardens of the villa, in the full glory of early autumn. Judith watched the cascading waters of the fountain as they caught and held rainbow colours from the sun.

She spoke at last into the silence, saying quietly as she addressed Alexis' back, 'Am I right in thinking it was you who decided Petros would be better off staying here?' The challenge in her voice was ignored for a long moment before Alexis slowly swung round with the smooth litheness with which Judith was by now so familiar. His dark Greek eyes met hers with direct candour.

'It does happen to be my opinion, yes.'

'The reason?' She was aware of Panos' interest as he waited for an answer.'

'Petros is with friends here, his relatives. In England he'd be with strangers.' So cool and confident. She could think what she liked, for all he cared, he seemed to be telling her, as once again there was a challenge in the air, but this time coming from him, instead of from Judith.

'You know very well that I won't stay here,' she told him decisively. 'If, Panos, you are really intending to leave your son here, then I am sorry, but you must get someone else to look after him.' She cast her eyes over to where Petros and Andreas were now playing, by the fountain, mischievously allowing the spray to drench them.

'I don't want to change his nanny,' began Panos with an uncertain glance at his brother-in-law. 'Petros is used to you, Judith, and I do not think you should allow any quarrel you happen to have with Alexis to influence you—'

'You don't know everything,' broke in Judith. 'If you did, then you would understand.' She threw Alexis a glance. 'Perhaps you would like to enlighten him as to the situation which has developed between us? I'll leave you—'

'No!' from Panos in a tone which could easily

have come from Alexis, so imperious was its inflection. 'Stay and we will discuss this matter!'

'Yes,' drawled Alexis unexpectedly and with a quality of mocking amusement in his voice, 'I will do as you ask, Judith, and enlighten Panos.' He transferred his glance to his brother-in-law, ignoring the look of near-panic which crossed Judith's face. 'I have asked Judith to be my pillow-friend. She'd very much like to, but at the same time she has some quite outmoded ideas about chastity—'

'Shut up!' She fumed, taking a step forwards and raising a hand as if she would like to strike him. 'How dare you ridicule me before Panos!'

'Is that all that's the matter with you?' Panos looked amazed. 'You've been his pillow-friend once, so why not again!'

She gasped and for a full half-minute was unable to speak. When she did it was to say, both with indignation and contempt, 'I was never his pillow-friend! And as for becoming that now— well, you here in Greece have your ideas, and we in Britain have ours—'

'In Britain?' with a sardonic lift of Alexis' eyebrows. 'In Britain, as anywhere else, there have been dramatic changes in ideas!'

'You must have been his pillow-friend,' from Panos who had not really listened to the rest. 'You were engaged to Alexis, and even in Greece engaged couples sleep together, for the engagement is, in effect, the marriage. It's a church occasion here—'

'In my country the engagement is *not* the marriage!' retorted Judith, hot with embarrassment. 'And now, if you will excuse me! I am not

willing to stand here and be insulted! Panos—
get someone else for your son—and quickly!'
And with that she swept from the room, her
cheeks burning, but in her heart the sadness of
failure and frustration. She only now fully
realised just how much she wanted to go on
looking after Petros. She had been looking forward to living in Berkshire . . . had in fact,
though almost unconsciously, been regarding
with anticipation that which was exceedingly
pleasant: the renewal of her friendship with
Leslie. She could not find a reason for the
change that had come over her, and the only
feasible explanation was that she felt the need of
a close companion, someone she could think of
as dependable and affectionate.

She went from the villa into the garden and
joined the children. Both came bounding up to
her, Petros clinging to her skirt and tugging it as
he spoke with pleading eagerness, asking her to
play with them.

'Of course,' she agreed with a smile that had
to be forced. 'What are we going to play?'

'Hide-and-go-seek!' exclaimed both boys in
unison, their voices ringing out so that she knew
they would carry through the open window of
the room she had just left.

'You be it, Judith!' from Andreas, who had
begun to run already. 'Hide your face—and don't
peep between your fingers!'

She laughed and did as she was bid, putting
her hands to her eyes. When she withdrew them
they were wet. . . .

She had no intention of dining with the two
men. But neither did she relish the thought of

having her meal alone in her room. This was Leslie's last evening, and without hesitation she phoned him at his hotel. They had already said good-bye, but she was far too restless to stay in, even though it was not one of her evenings off. As before, she asked the women to keep popping upstairs to see that Petros was all right.

'Lovely to see you!' exclaimed Leslie on meeting her in the lobby of his hotel. 'How come?' His eyes were admiring, the clasp of his hand a comfort to her at a time when she needed to be comforted.

'I'm on duty, but I couldn't stay in.'

'Something wrong?' With a gentle hand beneath her elbow, he guided her to a secluded table in the lounge and called a passing waiter. After ordering the drinks he asked again if anything was the matter. Judith paused in indecision, but not for long. She poured out the whole story, watching Leslie's changing expression as his face registered several emotions from anger and indignation to sympathy and anxiety.

'Come back with me tomorrow,' he begged, but Judith shook her head even before he had finished speaking.

'That's impossible, Leslie. I must stay until proper arrangements are made for Petros— No, please don't interrupt, even though you believe I'm being sentimental and silly over the little boy. I'm not, Leslie, believe me. He's asking for his mother, just as he was asking for his father. In Greece, families are very close, and it's not going to be good for Petros when he realises that his mother's gone for good.'

'He's very young,' began Leslie.

'And very intelligent. In any case, three and a

101

half is not a baby stage anymore. Children today are more grown-up than you and I were. Parents don't seem to want their children to remain babies for any longer than is necessary these days.' A sad note had entered her voice. She thought she would keep her children young for just as long as possible . . . if she ever had any children—a remote possibility, for even though her feelings for Leslie had changed somewhat, she still could not see herself married to him. But perhaps this aching love she had for a man who would never marry her would eventually die.

'It will take a long time, though,' she said with a heavy sigh.

'What?' Leslie looked questioningly at her. 'What did you say, dear?'

She gave a start. 'I was talking to myself,' she answered, faintly bewildered that she could have spoken aloud. 'It was nothing.'

'You're very upset tonight,' he observed, eyeing her speculatively. 'But it's understandable under the circumstances. No girl can take that sort of treatment without feeling upset—no decent girl, that is.'

She smiled wanly at him. 'I shouldn't have told you everything,' she said.

'I'm glad you did. It does one good to get things off one's mind, and you do have a sympathetic listener, Judith, and one you can trust not to repeat anything you have told him.'

She nodded. There was no one he could repeat it to, anyway.

They were just about to begin the second course when Judith, glancing up, gave a little cry of surprise and dismay.

'What—?' Leslie had turned to follow the direction of her gaze. 'That man!' he said grittingly. ' Well, take no notice—'

'How can I?' she cut in quiveringly. 'I ought not to be out!'

Alexis, followed closely by his brother-in-law, was being shown to a table not far from where Judith and her companion were sitting. Black fury out of all proportion looked out from Alexis' eyes, while Panos, unaware that Judith had no right to be there, merely smiled and sat down.

Alexis came over to their table, his dark accusing eyes fixing hers, disconcerting her even more than she was disconcerted already. 'What's the meaning of this?' His glance swept over her companion. 'Have you once again forgotten your duty?' His voice was hard, and so were his eyes as he switched his attention back to Judith. She coloured hotly but, exceedingly conscious of Leslie's fixed and angry stare, she lifted her chin and brought a sparkle to her eyes.

'I have given in my notice,' she said brusquely. 'I also consider I'm staying on only to oblige both you and Panos. Therefore, I feel no obligation to stay in every evening—or *any* evening,' she amended on noting his sudden raising of those straight black brows. 'Petros cannot possibly come to any harm, not with so many people to watch over him. You're unreasonable, Alexis, in expecting me to stay in on my own.' Her voice was quietly controlled, but contained a quality of determination which, she thought, should suppress any further argument which Alexis might have thought of making.

She saw his jaw flex, his mouth compress,

heard his harsh voice say briefly, 'I'll speak with you later!'

'Well!' exploded Leslie when Alexis had gone.

'He's right,' Judith said unhappily. 'I ought not to have come out.'

'But I don't understand why you aren't free every night. If these women can look after Petros on one evening, then why can't they look after him every evening?'

A reasonable argument to anyone who did not fully understand her duties, thought Judith, who said after a pause, 'It isn't their job to baby-sit, Leslie. Each week I have four evenings free, which is what Helen gave me. I agreed to stay in the other three, so I am to blame, not Alexis, who has every reason to be angry.'

'He's not angry, only jealous!'

'You think so?' Judith's eyes wandered towards the table where Alexis sat, opposite his brother-in-law.

'I'm sure of it. He wants you, as you've told me, and so it's natural that he's jealous of me. What I don't understand is why the devil he doesn't marry you—' He stopped and coloured up. 'You don't want to marry him, of course, do you?'

She hesitated, then shook her head. 'No,' she lied, 'I don't want to marry him.' Was it a lie, though? she was asking herself only seconds after telling herself that it was. Did she want to marry Alexis knowing he did not and never would love her? She shirked the answer and concentrated on the delicious meal which was set before her.

A *bouzouki* band began to play and several

couples rose and went onto the small dance floor. When Judith and Leslie had finished the main course, he asked her if she would care to dance. She shot a glance at Alexis, then said, rising from her chair just as Leslie did the same, 'I'd love to,' and slipped into his arms.

They danced close together, not doing any particular steps. She was all the time acutely aware of Alexis' eyes upon her, burning into her, and she dared not meet them . . . was afraid to meet them.

And that was because she was sure that Alexis would, with his keen perception, know at once that she was wishing it were he who was holding her so close. . . .

He came to her as she finished the dessert. A slight bow, a possessive hand beneath her elbow, an imperious ring to the words: 'Shall we dance, Judith?' And before she could even produce a flashing thought as to whether or not she would accept the invitation, she found herself on her feet, urged with a kind of gentle coercion, and she was swung away from the table, leaving Leslie gaping, as surprised as she by the swiftness of the incident.

'You have no right—' she began.

Alexis quietly interrupted her with: 'Relax, my dear, and enjoy the dance. It's a long while since you and I danced together, but, if I remember correctly, we performed very well together— especially when we were as close as this—' He drew her against him, so close that she was conscious of the hard muscles of his thighs, the shape of his body, the sudden throb of his maleness. Vainly she tried to pull away, but he was determined to keep her close, melding their bodies so that they moved as one. Embarrassed, with the blood surging into her cheeks and temples, Judith felt that every eye must be upon them, and that every Greek man present must be affected by the sensuous way in which Alexis was behaving. He was all Greek at this moment, primitive and uncaring, masterfully letting her see that he would do with her as he pleased. Shaken and wanting only to escape, she made another attempt to pull away.

'You'll have people staring at you,' warned Alexis. 'Stop drawing attention to yourself.'

'Attention must already be drawn to *us!*' she flashed. 'Let me go! Take me back to the table!'

'Relax,' he advised again. 'I can't recall that you were such a prude before.'

She drew a breath but made no answer. Better, she decided, to say no more, but to finish the dance and hope the music would not go on too long. She relaxed, and to her amazement soon found herself enjoying the dance, found herself recalling those idyllic days and weeks of her engagement . . . a lovely interlude in her young life when she had believed she was beloved by this tall dark Greek who was holding her so possessively. Yes, a lovely interlude . . . but now . . .

She continued to enjoy the movement of their bodies—her own and his—in spite of the memories becoming faintly bitter. Undoubtedly Alexis had an easy way of affecting her senses, her emotions . . . her defences.

'Are you going to stay and look after Petros?' The words were a whisper close to her lips as he bent his head to voice them. She fluttered long, curling eyelashes and peeped at him through them. Had he caught his breath—or had she imagined it?

'You know I'm not staying.' Words coming from the brain, where common sense prevailed —but what of her heart? Her vulnerable heart . . . and Alexis was well aware of it, she decided. Yet, somehow, she hoped he did not know that she loved him. Let him believe it was the physical attraction which he exerted over her. Better that than for him to know she had fallen in love with him all over again.

'You'd desert that little boy?' Again the words were whispered close to her mouth. She felt his cool clear breath, inhaled the male aroma of him . . . a heady after-shave mingling with the smell of newly laundered linen . . . and the sense-stirring masculine smell that was beyond description but added to his attractiveness as a man.

'Superlative' was the only way she could describe him: a king amongst men, descendant of those superb athletes of ancient Greece . . . and of the pagans, whose gods in their amourous exploits often fathered mortals. Was Alexis one of those whose ancestors were descended from the gods? He could be descended from the mighty Zeus himself, she mused, so completely lost in her magical reverie that she jumped on hearing his voice again.

'You haven't answered me, Judith. Where have you taken that mind of yours this time?' He was amused; he showed it in his expression and by the quirk of a lip.

'I can't stay, Alexis,' she told him and had no notion of the flat despair contained in her voice.

'It isn't a question of deserting Petros, but of leaving you . . . while I am safe.'

He laughed softly, his dark head bent so that his cheek was caressing hers. 'Do you think you will ever be safe from me?' he enquired gently.

'What an opinion you have of yourself, Alexis! Do you suppose I let you dominate every single moment of my waking hours?'

'I wouldn't be surprised, for you . . .' He trailed off, and when she looked up he was frowning darkly.

What had he been about to say? Could it possibly have been: '. . . for you dominate mine'?

Judith caught her breath at the idea. But if he was so deeply affected, then surely what he felt for her was something far stronger than mere physical attraction. She realised she had said something like this to herself before. . . . Yes, this was the second time that the idea had occurred to her that Alexis' feelings for her were more than what he would have her believe. Again she was asking herself why he did not want to marry her. And again, after much pondering, she found no answer to her question, but coming forcefully into her mind and remaining there was the conviction that it was not love in the true sense which he felt for her, simply because—she told herself—Alexis was not capable of any deep love.

'Let us go outside.' His lips were still close, the persuasion of their utterance supplemented by their touch on hers. She wondered what Leslie was thinking, and feeling.

'No!' she said at once, the refusal as angry as it was brief.

'You'll do as I wish!' And without more ado Alexis was almost roughly propelling her towards the open French window, beyond which was darkness, silent and complete.

'No!' she flashed again, but she did not struggle—not here, where she and he were in full view of everyone in the restaurant.

Once outside she turned on him, her voice vibrating with anger. 'Who do you think you are—dominating me like this? I'm going back in there—at once!'

'Not yet,' he asserted with infuriating calm. 'I want two things from you, my dear Judith: a kiss and a promise.'

'You'll get neither!'

'You're wrong. I shall get both.'

She freed her hand from his and ran blindly forwards into the blackness of the grounds, hair flying, feet lifting high because she had soon realised that tree roots were tangled along the ground.

'Judith—come back! Stop, you little fool!' He sounded concerned, she thought, and she was gratified. She continued to run without knowing where she would end up. Too late she realised she should have taken the other direction, making her way towards the lights of the building. She was instead running away from them, and soon she felt herself to have left the lawns and the shrubberies and entered the wild part of the grounds, the wooded part where undergrowth was thick and high about her legs. Her breath was giving out; she stumbled but righted herself again, vitally conscious of Alexis, coming after her but not quite sure just where she was in this black world of almost primitive vegetation. She felt a root catch her sandalled foot, stabbing painfully into her toes. She went forwards, crying out and spreading her hands. Alexis lifted her; she leant against his chest, her sobbing breath almost choking her.

'You—brute!' she burst out, enraged and frightened. 'You ought to be ashamed of yourself!'

'Dear Judith,' he said with some asperity, 'you have only yourself to blame. You had no need to run from me as if I were about to rape you!'

'Weren't you?' she managed, between gasping breaths.

'Out here?' She could almost see the quizzical lift of those straight black brows. 'Have a bit of sense, child. In any case, there'd not have been time. Leisurely love-play and pleasant, romantic surroundings make for increased pleasure—'

'Stop being so frivolous!' she snapped. 'Keep your wit for people like Camille . . . your mistress!'

To her surprise he only laughed, then bent his head and kissed her full on the lips.

'Come, Judith—' His voice was suddenly very gentle, his hand, stroking her hair, almost tender in its caress. 'Are you feeling all right? We must go back—'

'It's not my fault we're here at all!' She was still angry but, paradoxically, she wanted to stay here, resting in his strong, supporting arms, thrilling to the feel of his hard body, to the touch of his hand on her hair.

'No, it's my fault,' he agreed, still holding her close. 'Did you hurt yourself?' He sounded anxious, she thought—and almost wished she *were* hurt, just so she could make him feel guilty and contrite.

She was truthful, though, and said she was not hurt. 'But I'm out of breath and scared,' she just had to add finally.

'Scared?'

'Of the dark!'

He laughed against her cheek. 'Not of me? That's a relief.'

'You'd like me to be afraid of you,' she accused, pulling out of his arms, albeit reluctantly. 'Come on. Leslie will be wondering what on earth's happening, and so will Panos.'

'Panos will be drawing his own conclusions,' returned Alexis with a hint of mirth.

'*Greek* conclusions!'

'Certainly the wrong conclusions.'

'Do Greeks never think of anything but *that*?'

'Unfortunately, when one has a business to attend to, one has to think of other things.'

'Stop making fun of me!'

'Certainly, my dear. I shall now have the kiss I mentioned. . . .' His mouth found hers in the darkness, his warm hands having reached out to take her shoulders in a firm grip. 'Kiss me, Judith. You know you want to.'

She did as she was told, and this time it was not because she wanted to, but because she wished to satisfy him in order to get back to the restaurant without any further delay.

'Satisfied?' she asked tartly when he drew away.

'Not by a long chalk.' He possessed her mouth again, this time moistly caressing, using

111

his expertise, forcing her lips apart, exploring the sweetness of her mouth until at last she was robbed of the last vestige of resistance. She pressed herself to him, reciprocating to his kisses, his insistent movements, the caress of hands that so easily awakened emotions and continued to heighten them. 'That was better,' he was saying after long moments of rapturous silence. 'So much for the kiss. . . . And now the promise —will you stay and care for Petros?'

'I—'

'If I promise not to molest you?'

'You couldn't keep a promise like that if you tried!' she shot at him as the reminder of several promises already made and broken.

'Your fault, for being so tempting.'

'Is that supposed to be flattery?'

'It was a statement—a true one.' He paused, but she held a rather frigid silence.

He went on to press for an answer to his question, repeating it with a distinct note of persuasion in his voice: 'Will you stay and care for my nephew?'

'No. . . .' She shook her head, but weakly. 'I'd like to, I admit, but . . .' Again she shook her head. 'It wouldn't work.'

'We'll *make* it work.' He was still holding her, but at arm's length now, and his eyes seemed to be fixing hers in the darkness. 'I make a most solemn promise this time, Judith. I shall not molest you in *any* way at all.'

'You won't even kiss me?'

There was a pause and she guessed at the sardonic amusement in his eyes.

'Not unless you want me to,' he said, then instantly put his fingers to her lips to stem the retort which he obviously guessed had leapt to them. When a suitable amount of time had passed, he removed his hand and said seriously, 'Well, Judith, do I have your promise in exchange for mine?'

Still she hesitated, yet within her was the conviction that to hold out against him would be futile. She said at last, in a voice of resignation not unmingled with tiredness, 'All right; I'll stay for a little while.'

'A little while?' She knew he was frowning.

'How long I stay depends on how you behave,' she said forthrightly.

'You're afraid of temptation, aren't you?'

'I shan't answer that. Shall we go back now?'

He made no answer, but in silence he took her arm and guided her safely through the high undergrowth, holding her firmly in case she should trip again. She thought: *If only he could care. . . .*

An impossibility, she decided, the weight of dejection settling on her. She ought to have held out against all his persuasions and promises, ought to have used her common sense and made a firm decision to go home.

'Let me look at you before we go in there.' Alexis spoke as they came into the glare of the hotel lights. 'No, you don't seem to be in any way dishevelled. However, borrow my comb—' He took it from his pocket and handed it to her.

'Thank you.' She used it and handed it back, then began to walk on again.

'And thank you,' he said quietly, 'both for the kiss and the promise.'

113

Chapter Five

Tears welled up in Judith's eyes as she watched Panos saying a final good-bye to his son. Petros had been told, very gently by Judith, that his daddy was going away again and Petros had instantly burst into tears.

'Why is he going?' sobbed the child, pressing into Judith's arms and clinging to her blouse. 'And where's my mummy? Why did she go away all this time? You said she'd come back soon!'

Judith had done her best to comfort him and succeeded in some measure. But now came the parting she had dreaded. She and Alexis were there, in the salon, both uncomfortable, both angry with Helen, but whereas Alexis put the whole blame for the broken marriage on her, Judith felt that at least some of the blame lay with Panos. He was too pompous and full of his own importance. And unlike Alexis, whose arrogance savoured more of nobility and the superiority that came from a long line of aristocracy, Panos' personality was of the blustering type; he was brash and he was also conceited. Alexis was not like that at all, and as she compared them Judith felt that there had been some excuse for Helen's action in leaving Panos. However, there was no excuse for her leaving her little boy.

For several hours after Panos had left the

villa, Petros was inconsolable, and both Judith and Alexis were with him the whole time.

But at last Judith got him to bed and to sleep, watched anxiously by Alexis, who even went into the nursery and stood there while Judith, in soft and soothing tones, told him a fairy story. When eventually he was lulled to sleep and she turned tired and anxious eyes to the man standing there, it was to see the most odd expression on his face.

'He'll be all right now—well, for tonight, at least,' she said reassuringly. 'He never wakens once he's gone off.'

'But tonight might be different.'

'I don't think so. Anyway, I shall be here if he should happen to waken.'

Alexis would not let her stay by the bed, though. 'I'll send Androula up,' he decided. 'She's very fond of him and will not mind staying with him.' He looked down into Judith's face and her heart gave a little lurch when she saw his smile, for it was almost tender, and in his dark eyes that strange unfathomable expression remained. 'You need a rest,' he said. 'Have half an hour on the bed and then join me for dinner.'

'Thank you. . . .' she murmured, scarcely knowing what she was thanking him for— providing Androula to relieve her, advising her to rest on the bed, or inviting her to dine with him. She was too weary and upset to think clearly at all, and it was a real relief to lie down and relax.

She later took a bath and it was this which really refreshed her so that when she joined

Alexis at half past eight he glanced at her in surprise.

'You're obviously feeling better,' he observed, his eyes lifting to the shining glory of her hair, then down again to her face.

'I rested, as you recommended, then had a bath. It's surprising what a comfort it is to lie in warm, scented water. . . .' Her voice trailed off and soft colour spread into the delicate contours of her cheeks, for Alexis was making no attempt to hide his thoughts. He was visualising her naked in the bath! 'It was a bubble bath!' she added, and her colour heightened even more when he burst out laughing.

'Shy. . . .' His voice carried a strange inflection. 'I never realised just how shy.'

'I'm not shy, but you embarrass me,' she complained like a child who has a grievance against a grown-up. 'You have a one-track mind, Alexis.'

'I have already said you're far too tempting— and no more so than when you blush like this.' He looked deeply into her eyes. 'How do you expect me to keep that promise I made?'

'Perhaps,' she returned, trying to hide her nervousness, 'I had best not dine with you, or even come into your company. I could eat in my room—'

'I'm sorry if I frightened you,' he said, surprising her. 'I've not the slightest intention of breaking my promise.'

Reassured, she was able to ease back against the upholstery and enjoy the drink which Alexis handed to her. Later, over dinner he mentioned the cruise which he had told her about and on which he had intended taking his sister.

'I think it will be a good thing for Petros,' he went on with a veiled expression in his eyes. 'It will take his mind off his parents, don't you agree?'

Judith felt her pulses tingle. 'It would certainly be a treat for him,' she agreed, deliberately avoiding any reference to what her own role might be.

'He would need his nanny with him, of course.' Casually he helped himself to more vegetables from a dish that was standing over a small flame. 'You'd like to take a cruise?'

Danger lights shooting into her brain! 'Androula might like to look after Petros,' she began, then stopped at his expression.

'You are my nephew's nanny,' was his softly spoken reminder.

'I don't think I want to go on a cruise just now.'

'Afraid again?' with a quizzical lift of his brows.

'I'd be a fool to go on a cruise with you!'

'Nonsense. You'd enjoy every moment of it.'

She looked at him suspiciously. 'Petros could manage without a nanny if he had you,' she stated. 'There isn't any need for me to go on this cruise—and you know it.'

'You believe I can look after the child?' he said in surprise. 'Don't be ridiculous. And stop suspecting me of having ulterior motives for everything I do. I'm taking that cruise and Petros goes with me . . . and so do you.'

She gave a sigh of resignation, accepting that, after all, it was not unreasonable of Alexis to expect her to accompany her charge, no matter where he went.

When dinner was over she excused herself and went out into the garden, where all was cool and fresh after the rather sultry warmth of the day— and especially the afternoon, when the strong sun had shone unhindered by any vestige of clouds. Striking along the mountainsides, the brilliant light it gave off intensified the impression of heat and it was a relief when its brilliancy began to fade. Now, in the cool moonlight, the atmosphere was idyllic, magical, like something from fairyland. The fountain still cascaded down into the ornamental pool, making music to mingle with the incessant trill of cicadas in the olive and carob trees. Judith felt totally at peace, deliberately putting from her mind any doubts she might have about the risks involved in the forthcoming cruise. Romantic the setting might be, but all she had to do was keep out of harm's way ... 'harm' being Alexis.

She swung round, nerves tingling.

She should have known he'd come out here! Luck seemed always to be with him! Escape? No chance, she admitted, biting her lip in vexation at her own stupidity in coming out here in the first place.

He said as he reached her, 'Care for a stroll onto the site?'

The Sanctuary, sacred and pulsating with the atmosphere of past glories, hallowed and haunted by ghosts of gods and heroes and suppliants. . . . Moonlight on Temple and Treasuries and the vast amphitheatre rising to the clouds. Towering mountains, where eagles nested. . . .

She shook her head and said no; she was far too tired to go all that way.

'All that way?' The dark eyes were mocking.

'What I mean is—the garden's far enough at this time of night.' Prickles were running along her spine, for he was looking at her in a way which made her extremely nervous.

'It's early,' he said and took a step closer. She stared up at him, noting the irony in his gaze, the quirk of humour that lifted one corner of his mouth. Her eyes lifted and she was looking at the sleek blackness of his hair above the noble forehead, the straight, classical nose, the rigid jawline that denoted the quality of the autocrat in him. She quivered and scarcely knew the reason. Fear or some other emotion? Why was it that one man above any other she had ever met could affect her in this way? He sent her all to pieces so that her legs felt like jelly. Some woman one day was to be so thrilled to have him for her husband . . . and for her lover. . . .

Dejection dropped on her like a leaden weight; she turned away from his gaze and murmured flatly, 'I'll be going in. It'll turn chilly, I think.'

'What a lame excuse.' Alexis' voice quivered with laughter.

'Call it that if you wish.' Judith was past caring about his perception.

'Come for a stroll. It'll do you good.' He took her arm and she made no attempt to jerk from his hold. Easier by far to comply . . . and certainly more pleasant.

She sighed deeply, wishing she were of a stronger personality so that she could put up some kind of a fight against this attraction he had for her. She was like a jellyfish, no backbone.

They went onto the site and found themselves

alone there—alone with the deep silence, and the spirits of long-departed gods.

'It—does something to you.' Judith's voice was a husky little whisper.

'Like what?'

'Perhaps you don't feel it, because you're used to it,' she said, forgetting his question. 'But for me—well, it's magical and awesome, appealing and yet faintly threatening.'

'Threatening?' He stopped and turned her round to face him. 'In what way, threatening?'

'It's difficult to explain,' she answered vaguely. 'At times I feel the gods don't really want me here, trespassing on their sacred terrain.'

A low laugh escaped him. 'You really do believe in the gods, don't you?' he said.

'How could anyone not believe?' she countered. 'The spirits of the past are definitely here; everyone says so.'

'Everyone?'

'I've read a good deal about Delphi since I came and it is very apparent that the Sanctuary has a most profound effect on all who visit it.' Her voice was low and reverent, her eyes in the moonlight big and bright and faintly bewildered. 'There are so many things we mortals do not understand.'

His hands were still on her shoulders. He hesitated and she knew why. She should draw away and in so doing convince him that she was not in the same mood as he. But instead she stood there, waiting . . . and vitally aware of the growing excitement within her. Time went on and yet, paradoxically, it stood still.

'I promised,' he said with a deep sigh and

took his hands from her shoulders. 'Come, let us walk . . . or else . . .'

They boarded the *Santa Maura* the following Saturday in Pireaus and it sailed out of the harbour in brilliant sunshine.

'Petros seems to have recovered very well,' observed Alexis, glancing down at him as all three of them stood by the rail.

Judith nodded her agreement, her eyes turning to where the child was standing a few feet away, waving frantically to no one in particular on the waterfront.

'But what will be the end of it, Alexis?' she asked, speaking her thoughts aloud. 'Children always suffer when a marriage breaks up, and it isn't fair.' The sadness in her voice was not lost on him and he turned swiftly, to look down at the top of her head.

'Don't take it too much to heart, Judith,' he said and there was a tenor of gentleness which she had never expected. 'There is nothing more you can do for Petros. You're doing a fine job— and I thank you.'

She looked up and produced a wan smile. 'I don't agree with Panos' going back to Portugal.'

'Neither do I,' returned Alexis grimly. 'I tried to persuade him to stay, but apparently the business of making money was more important than the welfare and happiness of his son.' He gave her a brief smile before responding to the insistence of his nephew, who wanted him to look at a young child who was paddling a canoe.

'Can I have one of those?' Judith heard him ask.

'When you've grown a bit,' was Alexis' reply.

'I could do what he's doing!'

'You're not going to have the chance,' said Alexis, but gently, as he put a hand on the boy's curly head. 'That boy is a lot older than you.'

'How old is he?'

'About ten.'

'I can't wait till I'm ten, Uncle Alexis. It's too long.'

'You have to learn to swim first,' put in Judith with a smile. 'Uncle Alexis will teach you while we're on this cruise. There's a lovely big pool on the deck above this.'

'I saw it.' Petros gave a sigh as his attention returned to the boy in the canoe. He was doing very well, thought Judith, but her interest was soon somewhere else. She loved the bustle of a dockside, and here in Pireaus the activity was at its height, with ships being unloaded and smaller ones—obviously pleasure craft—bobbing about, tugging at their moorings. A cruise ship, white and blue, was at the dockside, having finished a Mediterranean cruise similar to the one which the *Santa Maura* was about to begin. It was being cleaned and fitted out ready for the next cruise, which would probably start the following day. The ferry *Knossos* was taking on passengers bound for the islands of Rhodes and Cos, while the *Lindos* was lying at anchor, probably having come from a run to Aegina and Hydra. The glamour of the scene was intriguing to Judith.

Alexis, noticing her expression as she leant on the rail, smiled faintly as he said, 'There's a look of total absorption on your face. It is quite an ordinary, everyday scene, you know.'

She turned and shrugged her shoulders. She was in an apple-green cotton dress, tight fitting and sleeveless, and she had a white kid bag slung over her shoulder. The breeze was playing tricks with her hair and also giving fresh, healthy colour to her cheeks. Alexis' eyes were riveted on her after their flickering, yet comprehensive, glance over her body.

'Yes, I do know. But to me the bustle of life is always interesting. I love to watch people and note their activities in certain circumstances.' She paused, but he did not speak. 'One can never be bored if one has an interest in what others are doing.'

It was some moments before Alexis spoke, and when he did there was an almost tender inflection in his voice which sent her pulses racing. 'You're nice, Judith . . . quite exceptional.'

'Is—is that flattery?' she asked, her colour rising in the most attractive way.

His glance became lazily mocking. Judith had the strange and unfathomable impression that he had suddenly forced himself to become guarded. 'Call it what you will. It was in fact a mere observation gained by your words.' Lifting a hand, he stifled a yawn. 'I'm going down to my stateroom. I shall see you at dinner. The table number's six—you haven't forgotten?'

She shook her head, glancing down to where Petros had his fingers tightly wound round those of his uncle.

'I think we shall stay here for a while,' she said. 'Petros is enjoying himself.'

'And so are you.' He turned, tugging at his hand. Petros held on tightly.

'Don't go yet,' Petros begged. 'I want you to

stay with Judith and me.' His big, dark brown eyes were lifted in childish pleading which Judith knew instinctively Alexis would not ignore. The smile that came slowly to his lips had an almost devastating effect on Judith, causing, as it did, her heart to give a great lurch. How well she remembered that smile and the things it did to her!

'Very well, for a little while.'

Judith just had to ask the question that had been hovering on the edge of her mind since the moment Alexis had told her they were to go on the cruise.

'Alexis . . . it seems very strange to me that your—er—girl friend isn't to be with you at a time like this. Why isn't she?' The moment it was out Judith was regretting it, and her heightened colour was more than enough to tell him so.

His flickering glance reflected the amusement coming through in his voice as he said, 'I appreciate your interest, Judith. Are you by any chance commiserating with me?'

'Forget what I said!' Her voice was acid. 'I admit to speaking out of turn.'

'Camille,' he said slowly and quietly, 'will be joining us in Rhodes, where we dock and stay for about twelve hours. She isn't with me now because she's been away visiting her father in New York.'

Judith's colour began to ebb as she absorbed the full significance of the news he had given her. Camille here, on this ship, with Alexis. . . . What would her own place be then? Judith asked herself, conscious of the dead weight of dejection settling on her. For although at first she had genuinely not wanted to risk taking the cruise, once she had become used to the idea she had actually come to be thrilled by the prospect, and she knew now that, subconsciously, she had half-hoped that the romantic atmosphere might just do something to Alexis, and to his feelings towards her. . . .

But now she was to become the nanny in the true sense of the word, her role being nothing more than that of caring for the little boy while being forced to be the unwilling onlooker in a situation she would now do anything to avoid. If only she could get off the ship! But that was impossible; she had to remain on it for two full weeks.

That evening she had half a mind not to dine with Alexis, but to have the meal brought to her stateroom. It adjoined a smaller room occupied by Petros, and to one side, off a tiny corridor, was a luxurious bathroom. The stateroom itself was the last word in taste and planning, and she could realise—having made a cursory examination of the rest of the ship—just why Alexis was so proud of this latest addition to the impressive fleet which his company owned. However, as Petros was very tired and went off to sleep almost as soon as his dark head touched the pillow, she decided to go to the dining-room, after all. The evening would drag on interminably if she were to stay here on her own.

As she showered her mind quite naturally went over the last few days when she had been excitedly preparing for the cruise, buying bikinis and a new one-piece swimsuit, several sun tops and shorts, both brief, both matching, several evening dresses, and a couple of long skirts and dainty blouses. And now she was so deflated that she felt like relieving her pent-up emotions by having a good cry.

However, she resisted the temptation, logically aware that it would do no good at all; on the contrary, it would make her eyes red and swollen, so Alexis would instantly demand an explanation.

She chose an ankle-length skirt and one of the blouses—a white filmy thing with more substantial cuffs and collar in rich cream satin. Down the front of the blouse was dainty embroidery which included silver sequins skillfully dotted about to give the impression of glamour, and yet subtly subdued so that there was no question of anything vulgar or glaring. It had cost a great deal of money, but with hope in mind Judith had not begrudged one drachma. A waste, she now realised, since the hope had been crushed most effectively by those words uttered by Alexis when he told her that Camille would be joining the cruise.

She was conscious of eyes being arrested as she walked the length of the dining-room in the wake of the immaculately attired steward who was conducting her to table six.

She ought to have known it would be the captain's table. He was not there, of course, because his was the duty of getting the ship out of the harbour, and although that was already done, it was customary for the captain to be absent from dinner on the first night out. Judith arrived after three people were already seated. Two men rose and smiled; Alexis then introduced her to the people who would be sharing their table for the whole of the cruise. The couple were a Mr. and Mrs. Sternway, from Florida, who were on the last part of a six-month honeymoon. The woman on her own was Gloria Lovatt, a journalist who, Judith soon learnt, was intending to mix business with pleasure and write an article about the *Santa Maura*'s present cruise to five islands in the Mediterranean. She was a girl of medium height with a pale intelligent face and hair of a nondescript colour between dull brown and ash. She wore thick-lensed spectacles so it was difficult to see the colour of her eyes, but Judith felt sure they were grey, and serious. Wearing no rings at all, it seemed that she was neither married nor engaged. Judith was later to learn that Gloria had been married at eighteen and widowed eight years ago, when she was twenty. The couple were in their fifties, estimated Judith and was sure it was a second-time-round affair. This was to prove correct when, during dinner, they both mentioned their children, all married and with youngsters of their own.

'We thought we'd leave them to it,' laughed Ed, 'and get married.' He looked at his wife affectionately. 'Ruth wasn't sure, but I eventually persuaded her. I think she was tempted by the promise of this trip. We've been doing Europe and had a wonderful time, but now we're ready to go home. This trip is our final fling.'

His wife merely smiled. Judith, with her swift perception, saw that Ruth was puzzled as to the relationship existing between Alexis and herself. She had noticed Ruth glancing at her left hand, then at her face, and then transferring her interest to Alexis.

It was when the dessert course was served that Ruth, unable to contain her curiosity any longer, said with a bright smile, 'Are you two engaged?' She was looking at Alexis, but he made no comment.

There was a pause before Judith answered, 'No. I'm nanny to Mr. Vasilis' nephew who is with us.'

'Oh. . . .' Ruth seemed to be taken aback. 'Is this nephew in bed . . . or something?'

Judith had to smile. Glancing at Alexis, she saw the tight but amused smile on his lips.

'Yes, he's in bed.'

'They have watchers going round, I think.'

Judith nodded her head. 'They do, and so Petros is quite safe.'

'Petros. It's Greek for 'Peter,' we've learnt,' from Ed, who seemed to think he ought to contribute to the conversation. 'We met a Petros at our hotel in Athens. He was dining there with his wife—a charming lady, she was. But she didn't seem to have a Greek name to me. It was Helen.' He looked at Alexis. 'Is that Greek?'

Alexis' eyes narrowed. 'Some Greek women are called Helen,' he replied tautly. 'What was this lady like? She was charming, you said?'

'Oh, very!' from Ruth with bright eagerness. 'And they were so in love, weren't they, dear? We got into conversation with them in the bar and again afterwards when we were having our coffee in the lounge. They live in Athens, in an apartment, she was telling us, wasn't she, dear?'

'What was she like?' repeated Alexis, and something in his voice seemed to startle the couple for a space.

Gloria was interested, but not unduly so; she seemed to be happy with her own thoughts and had contributed very little to the dinner-time conversation.

'Tall and slender and dark, with big brown eyes and long straight hair. . . . Do you know this lady by any chance?' added Ed finally.

Alexis and Judith exchanged glances. It was some few seconds before Alexis said casually, 'I might, but the description fits thousands of Greek women.' He abruptly changed the subject, making it impossible for any further questions to be asked.

Chapter Six

The *Santa Maura* sailed into the harbour at Mykonos four days after steaming out of Pireaus, having called at two other islands en route. It was mid-afternoon and the sun shone brilliantly down from a cloudless Aegean sky. Judith was in shorts and a sun top, Petros in shorts and a T-shirt, while Alexis was in fine linen slacks and a conventional summer shirt of cotton, open at the throat and with the sleeves rolled up to above the elbows. It was amazing, thought Judith as she flicked him an upwards, sideways glance, how he invariably managed to appear immaculate no matter what he was wearing. His thick hair shone blacker than ever, it seemed, as the sun caught it—blue-black. His face was bronzed to the shade of matured teak, as were his hands and arms. Of course, his whole body was brown, owing to his nationality, and he had been the most noticeable and impressive male in the pool that morning when Judith, at a quarter past eight, with her small charge at her side, had gone for an early morning swim.

'Ready, young man?' Alexis' calm voice severed her musings and she turned, taking a step closer to him, pushing Petros before her.

'I don't like this part,' she said with a grimace.

'Being ferried ashore?' He gave an indifferent shrug. 'These *caïques* are as safe as the steamer.'

'Perhaps, but they're so small, and they rock about so.'

'I liked it last time!' from Petros, who was trying to ease himself in front of his uncle. 'I like little boats!'

Judith was glad when they were ashore and she had her feet on dry land. The spray had wet her hair and shoulders and she was seeking for a handkerchief when Alexis handed her one.

'Use this,' he said with a smile. 'Even if you find your own, it'll not be much good to you.'

She laughed and thanked him, her uplifted face aglow with health and happiness. Yes, she was happy, for the present; the past four days had been so pleasant that it seemed as if it were an impossibility that Camille should be putting in an appearance which would mar everything for Judith.

Alexis had Petros by the hand; with his other hand he guided Judith along the pier. She was dazzled by the whiteness of everything; even the streets had been whitewashed.

'They do the whitewashing twice a year,' Alexis told her when she commented on it.

'It's like being in an Alpine village!'

'Except for the temperature.'

'The sky seems darker because of the whiteness beneath it.' There were, of course, other colours: the greens of vines and other foliage; the pink and blue cupolas of the churches; the gay clothes of the tourists.

'Do you know your way round?' Judith was asking presently.

'I've been here before, so I think so,' Alexis answered. 'We go this way.' He was still holding Petros' hand. Judith took the other and it was only natural that she should think: *We're like a family . . . a married couple and their little son. . . .*'

What was Alexis thinking? she wondered, as they strolled along the esplanade, a crescent backing away from the sea. Was he, too, feeling the same way? A faintly bitter smile came to her lips and hovered there as she allowed her mind to create a picture of what might have been. By now they would probably have had three children—two boys and a girl would have been Alexis' choice, or even three boys. For Judith—well, she had always said she would not care what sex her children were so long as they were born perfect.

Alexis, glancing down at her, said quietly and with a curious inflection in his finely toned voice, 'Where are you now, my child?'

'Just thinking.'

'That's obvious. But where were your thoughts?'

Judith hesitated and did not know what prompted her to say, 'My thoughts were way back in the past.'

He raised his brows, a gesture which plainly proved that *his* thoughts had *not* been in the past. 'How far in the past?'

She swallowed and paused once again. 'It was nothing important,' she murmured.

And at that moment Petros broke in to say, 'What's that man doing with that thing?'

'It's an octopus. He's banging it on the ground to make it tender.'

'Ugh!' exclaimed Judith, shuddering.

'I was intending taking you into a *taverna* I know, where they specialise in octopus—'

'No, thank you, Alexis! I'll keep to the more conventional fish.'

'Look at all that lather!' Petros exclaimed.

'If you're talking to me, Petros, then no, I won't look!' Judith warned.

Petros chuckled. 'I'd like to do that. Will he let me, Uncle Alexis?'

'I do not intend to ask him.'

Judith gave her full attention to the native women tending their stalls where they were selling embroidery, carvings, sponges, and replicas of Greek gods and goddesses. Dressed in black, some of the older women seemed to have emerged from another era and seemed totally out of harmony with the gaiety of the holiday scene.

The sun was sliding down towards the horizon by the time they had wandered in and out of the bewildering network of narrow lanes and alleys that lay in a sort of half-hushed tranquillity behind the more fashionable façade of the waterfront. If tourists were in the habit of exploring these backwaters, then they certainly weren't doing so today. Judith commented on the quietness after pointing out a black-robed woman of ageless countenance sitting on a well-worn step, pounding some substance with the use of a pestle and mortar and Alexis informed her that this was not the height of the season.

'In effect,' he added, 'this is early autumn. In the full height of the season everywhere hereabouts would be crowded. Mykonos has quietened down a bit lately, but it is still the haunt of the jet-set. Very much so.'

'These alleyways so often end nowhere,' put in Petros as he trotted along between his uncle and his nanny. 'Why don't they lead to some place?'

'Well, originally they were made as sort of traps—'

'Traps?' Petros' big eyes became round with enquiry. 'What kind of traps?'

'Traps to catch pirates—'

'Ooh! Are there any pirates now?'

Judith glanced down at him and smiled. He was very English, she thought, but then he had been born and brought up in England, visiting Greece two or perhaps three times a year to see his relations. All this was as new to him as it was to Judith herself. She heard him ask, in his impeccable English, if they would see any pirates being caught in the traps.

'There are no pirates today,' was his uncle's patient reply. 'But in the old days there were plenty, and these particular traps were for pirates from other islands. The pirates from this island were the most feared, because no one could ever catch them.'

'Why?'

'Because they were too clever.'

'I'd like to be a pirate!'

Both Judith and Alexis laughed. 'You're a bloodthirsty young fellow!' Alexis glanced down at him. 'I don't know if I like you very much.'

It was Petros' turn to laugh. 'I know you like me,' he said, assurance ringing in his strong young voice. 'You like me because I'm nice!'

'My,' chipped in Judith with mock censure, 'you certainly have a very big head, Petros.'

At that he freed his hands and, chuckling, cupped them round his head.

'It's not big,' he asserted, peeping up at his uncle with mischief in his eyes.

'It'll be aching in a minute if I have any more of your cheek,' warned his uncle.

'You'd not cuff me! Mummy cuffs me sometimes. I wish my mummy and daddy were here,' he added with a sudden change of tone. 'How long will they be away, Judith?'

Silence. She glanced at Alexis. His mouth was tight, his profile forbidding, to say the least. He never now mentioned Helen.

'It could be a long time, darling,' Judith said gently at last when it became apparent that Alexis could find no words to answer the question. She guessed that at this moment it was anger that occupied his mind, to the exclusion of all else—anger against both parents, but mainly against Helen.

The sun was setting quickly now as they made their way back to the harbour. Petros—wearied by the walking and made even more tired by the breeze—was riding lazily on his uncle's back. As she looked at them, Judith could not help, once again, thinking of what might have been.

An involuntary impulse brought words tumbling from her lips which she instantly regretted. 'You look very much the doting father, Alexis.'

He turned his head, dark eyes filled with mockery. 'The female mind making pictures,' he said and laughed as he saw her blush.

'What sort of pictures does man's mind make at this moment?' she was able to retort after gathering up her composure with a swiftness that surprised her.

'At this moment?' His eyes flicked to the head resting on his left shoulder. 'It's of a woman being given the hiding she deserves.'

'Helen isn't wholly to blame.'

'Not wholly, but mostly.'

'No one can say that Panos is attractive.'

'Helen married him.'

'Because she had no choice. It was an arranged marriage. She told me so.'

'She had the right to object. All women have that right, even though many people like you have been given to understand otherwise.'

'They can object, yes. But what happens then? They immediately come under the most awful pressure from the whole family. It would take a strong personality to stand up against the threats—'

'Persuasions,' Alexis cut in to correct, but Judith shook her head.

'Threats, Alexis. From everyone—'

'You're talking about something you do not fully understand, Judith. A girl can object if she does not like the man chosen for her.'

'I know that if she were to refuse twice, then no other man would offer for her and so she would remain a spinster.'

'She could find a husband for herself.'

'Well, although she did not tell me at first that *her* marriage was arranged, Helen did tell me a lot during those few weeks. . . .' Judith's voice faded away to silence as embarrassment mounted within her. She ought to have avoided reference to their engagement, she thought with extreme vexation. However, she once more regained her composure and was able to continue: 'She told me a good deal about the customs of Greece, and it did seem to me that a girl is in a pretty sorry position if she happens to be born in this country—or any other country of the East, for that matter.'

'Have it your own way. You're entitled to your opinion. But even you cannot excuse or condone my sister's conduct in deserting her child.'

'I don't. As I once said, if my marriage broke up I'd take my child, or children, with me.' She was recalling his previous intimation that if such a situation affected him, then he would never allow his wife to take the children. However, to her relief he allowed the subject to drop, and in any case, they were nearing the pier and a *caïque* was waiting there to take passengers back to the ship.

It was to stay the night, and the following morning those who wanted could take the short trip over to the thinly inhabited island of Delos, sacred birthplace of Apollo, whose father, the mighty Zeus, had the island created by his brother, Poseidon, god of the sea, as a haven for the accouchement of Zeus' mistress, Leto, whom he had seduced and who later gave birth to twins, Apollo and his sister, Artemis. Leto had been wandering the earth in search of a place in which she could give birth to her children, but always she was turned away on the harsh orders of Zeus' jealous wife, Hera, and because all feared the queen of the gods, none would give sanctuary to the lonely, despairing Leto until her seducer in his pity counselled with Poseidon and the island of Delos rose from the sea, a rock formerly known as Adelos, the Invisible One.

'I love the mythology of Greece,' Judith was saying when, having put Petros to bed and made sure the minder would keep going in to look at him, she had joined Alexis in the lounge for a drink before dinner. 'My interest began when I was at school and these stories were given to us in the form of—well, fairy tales. They fascinated me because they seemed more fact than fiction, and they still seem real. I can still imagine, without difficulty, all these happenings taking place.'

To her surprise he nodded in agreement. She had expected him to scoff at what she had been saying, as he usually did.

'I suppose it seems real because of the very firm and sincere beliefs of the ancient Greeks in these numerous gods of Olympus.' He paused a moment and then went on: 'The island of Adelos was supposed to have been floating under the sea for a very long time before Poseidon raised it as a sanctuary for Leto.'

'So that was why it was called the Invisible One?'

He nodded. 'As a matter of fact,' he said with a grimace, 'Adelos was another of the lusty Zeus' mistresses. Her name was originally Asteria, a name very popular amongst Greek girls today. Asteria, being pursued by the god she did not want to associate with, turned herself into a quail, but Zeus then changed his form to that of an eagle in order to catch her. But she then changed herself into a rock which became submerged and remained just beneath the surface of the sea. This rock became known as Adelos.'

138

He ended on a note of amusement because of Judith's open-mouthed interest in what he was relating to her.

'I loved that story!' she exclaimed, hands clasped together, eyes wide and bright with eagerness.

And she had no notion of the effect she was having on the man sitting opposite her, the man who had jilted her because she had had a night out with another man.

'It isn't quite finished,' he murmured after a particularly long and intense pause. 'Asteria had eluded him, but Zeus, not to be outdone, turned his attentions to her sister, Leto—'

'Leto was Asteria's sister?'

'That's right, and Zeus, suspecting he might have the same difficulty in his efforts to seduce her as he had with her sister, decided to take on the form of a swan, in which guise he obviously met with more success.' Again that look of amusement, this time because his listener was frowning darkly.

'Zeus was a profligate,' she said. 'Not a likeable person—I mean, god,' she amended, and now she was laughing. 'Not very likeable at all.'

'His only real sin was in being slightly over-amourous,' Alexis returned, eyes dancing as he picked up his glass without taking his eyes off her face. He saw her eyes widen to their fullest extent.

'*Slightly* over-amourous!' She almost exploded. 'He was the most prolific seducer ever known!' The retort was out before she quite realised what she was saying and yet again the colour rose to tint her cheeks.

'You have an interesting phraseology,' was his unexpected comment, his gaze still fixed on her face. 'However, my dear, as this prolific seducer never even existed, it's rather a waste of time discussing him, isn't it?' He was actually teasing and she resented his attempt to disillusion her, to rob her of dreams which gave her such pleasure.

'I believe in him!' she bit back, eyes glinting in challenge.

'You're just a little girl, aren't you?' he murmured. His voice was so quietly tender that she scarcely caught the words, much less the subtle intonation. Yet she looked swiftly at him, her eyes widening to a question, her pulse rate increasing with the stirring of emotions in her heart. She seemed to be quivering with some vague unfathomable excitement, nerves tingling, mind reaching out . . . for what?

It was a profound moment of silence that followed his softly spoken words, an interlude of tension and, for Judith, of a groping through a mist, peering through eyes seeking and uncertain as to what they were seeking for.

'I—I think perhaps we—we ought to be going in for dinner,' she stammered, feeling very much the little girl he had just likened her to. 'The captain will probably be with us tonight, so we oughtn't to keep him waiting.' Tumbling words spoken to ease the tension, and she was not surprised to see the hint of amusement that lifted one corner of his mouth.

'You may be right—' He drained his glass and placed it on the low table which stood between them. He stood up, tall and straight and distin-

guished in the white jacket with the frilled blue
evening shirt and sophisticated bowtie. Judith
was in a Japanese-type dress with a high man-
darin collar above the embroidered bodice with
its tiny, handmade buttons. Brilliant red, it had
a slit right up to the thigh. At first it had been
Judith's intention to sew up this slit, but she had
been persuaded by a friend to leave it as it was.
To alter the dress in any way would take away
what the designer had taken so much time
over—the impression of something exotic and
sexy.

Alexis had already given his opinion of the
dress: delightfully feminine and tantalising.

She could not have said why she had decided
to wear it tonight. Was it to please Alexis? Whatever, it drew attention towards her as she and he
walked slowly and gracefully along the length
of the dining-room and sat down at their
table.

The captain arrived almost immediately,
bowed slightly in that charming way the aristocratic Greeks have, and sat down. The others
were already at the table. Conversation began,
quite naturally, with the various views on what
they had seen that day.

Judith and Gloria were the only two who had
not visited Mykonos before. Ruth loved it and
wanted to retire there. Her husband was enthu-
siastic about the island, but not in agreement
about retiring there.

'Too far from our families,' he pointed out.
'Visiting would cost too much and also would not
be often.'

'You could be right, dear.'

'And what about you, Miss Sommerville?

What did you think about Mykonos?' The captain's smile revealed several gold fillings.

'I liked it, but it's rather more touristy than I want for true attractiveness.'

'I agree.' Captain Melas' accent was so slight that it scarcely came through at all. He had been with Alexis' company for many years, and Judith had already guessed his age to be forty-eight to fifty. Of medium height, with broad, strong shoulders and not too much excess weight, he seemed most suitably fitted to be captain of a sophisticated cruise ship like the *Santa Maura*, with its shape and size and fittings all seeming to blend as a whole, with luxury and good taste as the all-important aspect which had obviously been firmly and most forcefully put over to the builders. Judith's eyes remained on the captain's dark face as he chatted with Gloria, having first politely asked if she had had an enjoyable day on the island. His features were rather rugged below a low forehead. And he had a shock of iron-grey hair immaculately clean and brushed back and to one side of his head. A gentlemen through and through, decided Judith, and wondered if he were married. She had not thought to ask Alexis, but she would.

The first course had been served by their steward, Mario, an Italian, one of many thus engaged in the dining room. Judith had asked Alexis if there was any especial reason for engaging more Italians as restaurant stewards than any other nationality—for there were no fewer than seventeen different nationalities represented amongst a crew of only about two hundred and fifty.

'They're polite without being obsequious, and the ladies are very partial to Italians.'

'They are?'

'The dark, handsome type who spells glamour and—er—excitement of a very special kind.' He gave her a whimsical glance which was reflected by the curve of his mouth.

Judith was now watching Mario as he served Gloria the meat she had ordered as part of the second course. The captain was talking to Gloria again, and Judith wondered if she were happy about the attention she was receiving. Gloria seemed shy, in a way, and yet she invariably found an intelligent and interesting answer for any question put to her. She toyed with her food, though, as if she lacked confidence when eating in public; she appeared to eat out of pure diversion at times, her whole manner introverted. Ruth, on the other hand, was typically an extrovert, the quick, impetuous speech which at times typified her manner being of the kind plainly designed to bring attention to herself.

The captain as usual invited them all to join him in the entertainment hall after dinner, his private table having the pride of place at the front and in the centre, facing the stage. First there was dancing, and it was Judith he chose as his first partner. She was nervous, being profoundly conscious that all eyes would quite naturally be on the captain, as they always were when he danced. Judith prayed she would not make any false steps or, horrifyingly worse, tread on his toes! All went well; she found herself following him in perfect harmony. When he thanked her at the end, she knew it was not from mere politeness, but because he had enjoyed the dance as much as she.

He then invited Gloria, who blushed as she rose, but yet seemed quite confident once she was on the floor.

'I'm puzzled about Gloria,' confided Ruth as her eyes followed the two swirling figures doing the waltz. 'She seems lonely and a bit unhappy, but she should have recovered from her loss long before now.'

'Loneliness can be so deflating to the spirit,' remarked Judith, who at times had felt lonely herself.

Alexis cast her a glance, speculative and strangely disconcerting.

It was later, as they were dancing, bodies closer than Judith would have wanted, that Alexis said without much expression, 'So you find loneliness deflating to the spirit?'

She leant away, a bewildered expression in her gaze. 'What exactly are you trying to say?'

'That your loneliness is self-inflicted.'

'So what about it? I'm captain of my own soul.'

'Don't snap at me,' he advised. 'I don't happen to be in a tolerant mood.' He drew her close again as another couple came near.

'I don't think I understand,' she said shortly. 'What's happened to make you so bad tempered?'

'This business of your loneliness—'

'I can't recall that I said I was lonely!'

'But you meant it.'

'Perhaps,' she conceded, then added challengingly, 'You obviously know of a cure for loneliness.'

'For *your* loneliness—if loneliness is the appropriate word. If you'd only relax, forget these darned prudish ideas of yours and start to live.'

She smiled to hide the anger rising within her. For her physical attraction was still the only draw she had for him, and it seemed he would never cease trying to have her as his pillow-friend.

'I do live, Alexis,' she returned mildly, 'in my own particular way, for there is a great deal more to life than sex.'

He drew an impatient breath, but his temper was swiftly cooling. 'Sex is popular the world over, yet you reject it. There's something positively abnormal about you! You do realise that?'

'Abnormal! I resent that! You can take it back if you please!'

'I'll do no such thing, because it's true.'

'I can't make you take it back,' she said tightly, 'but I can ask you to take *me* back to the table. I don't want to dance with you anymore!'

'But I want to dance with you. We shall continue till the music stops.'

'I've a good mind to trip you up!'

'Try it,' he challenged mockingly, 'and see how you fare.'

Her eyes glinted; she was being driven both by his manner and her own flaring temper. Deliberately she pushed her foot between his legs, jerking viciously and at the same time trying to thrust him away with her hands. The next instant she was crying out with pain and tears welled up in her eyes.

'You—brute!' she seethed.

The grip on her arms remained as tight and as cruel as a vice. 'Say you're sorry,' he ordered.

'Never!' Judith shut her eyes but the tears were already escaping through her lashes.

'You do ask for it, don't you?' His fingers dug in ruthlessly as he spoke. 'Are you going to apologise for trying to humiliate me?' Menacing the tone and very soft.

'Humiliate?' she echoed, her nerves on edge with the pain she was going through.

'I'd certainly have been humiliated if you'd succeeded in your attempt to off-balance me,' he said through his teeth, and she could imagine his thoughts. He was visualising himself sprawled on the floor, then rising to the titters of everyone in the vast room. She bit her lip, realising that she had given little thought to the results when she had, in her fury, acted so impetuously. 'Well,' prompted Alexis as those lean brown fingers let her feel even more of their merciless strength, 'are you going to drop that pride, or do I make you cry aloud?'

She swallowed, trying to rid her throat of the choking sensation which made speech so difficult. She looked up into his face, saw the hard, implacable tenseness of his features, the threat in his eyes, and she knew without any doubt at all that he would hurt her brutally if she delayed any longer in obeying his command. But it was with the greatest difficulty that she said at last, in husky, forced little tones, 'I'm sorry, Alexis.'

His fingers relaxed and such was the relief that more tears fell onto her cheeks. She would have hideous bruises, she thought, and suddenly it was white-hot fury which produced the flood of tears which rolled unchecked onto her cheeks and down to stain her lovely dress. Yes, water stained satin. . . .

'I hate you!' she breathed. 'Hate you—do you hear?'

She lifted her face, saw his startled expression, and heard him say abruptly, 'I didn't realise you were crying like that! We'd better go out on deck!'

And without waiting for either her agreement or protest, he swiftly guided her through the dancers, threaded his way amongst the tables, and eventually reached the door leading out onto the upper deck.

Chapter Seven

The following morning at nine o'clock they were boarding the *caïque* that would carry them to the tiny island of Delos. The occurrence of the previous night might never have happened for Alexis never mentioned it or referred to it even by a glance when he met Judith at the breakfast table.

The sea was choppy after a night of rain, but now the sun was shining from a nearly cloudless sky.

'Another small boat,' she commented with a grimace, knowing the *caïque* would be tossed about and she would be scared.

'Relax,' advised Alexis with a hint of amusement. 'The trip's short, so you'll not have to sit there clutching your seat for very long.' His glance skimmed her figure and she blushed in the knowledge that he liked what he saw. She wished she had worn a dress instead of bright blue shorts and a tight-fitting T-shirt.

She looked away, to make a cursory examination of the other passengers. Tourists, and most of them talking 'about anything and nothing,' as her Lancashire grandmother would have said, derision in her voice. Inane conversation, forced laughter, pretended knowledge about the archaeological site they were about to see. For herself, she meant to enjoy the trip, to feel—as she had in Delphi—the presence of past heroes and the pagan gods they had worshipped; their spirits were still there on Delos and would give the place a greater significance than would be seen on the surface. She meant to enjoy all the site had to offer, both palpable and impalpable. She had studied the island's history from the time of the third millennium, when it was settled by the Carians, through centuries of pagan worship, athletic games, and pilgrimages after the cult of Apollo had taken a firm hold upon the island and its inhabitants. After many vicissitudes during which the island was dominated by Athens, sacked by the Persians, and robbed of its treasures by the Romans, who also carried off its women and children into slavery, it finally became a pastureland for sheep farmers from nearby islands.

Today, after extensive excavations by archaeologists, its past glory lived again in some small measure. As Judith stepped ashore onto the small jetty which sheltered the little boats from the *meltimi*—'wind of the islands'—she was instantly sensitized to the atmosphere of times long past, although she was admitting that the sacred site lacked the grandeur of Delphi, where one always felt the presence of something profoundly sacred and knew that the words of the Romans still applied: *numen adist*—'a god is present here.'

'Ooh, look at all those lizards!' exclaimed Petros, who was naturally more interested in these giant lizards than in the fragments of ancient columns which they crawled over, col-

umns which were once part of the glorious
temples dedicated to the golden god, Apollo.
'Can you catch one for me, Uncle Alexis?'

'I don't think that would be easy,' he said with
a shake of his head. 'They appear to move
slowly, but if you should venture too close,
they'd run very quickly. But you've seen lizards
before, so you know how fast they can get out of
your way.'

'I've only seen little ones in your garden. And
in England we don't have any—only snakes
sometimes, adders and grass snakes.' His eyes
were on one particularly large and bloated lizard
perched, stock-still, on a broken column of lovely Pentellic marble which had belonged to the
second temple, the one built by the Athenians
for the exclusive worship of the sun god, whose
Holy Sanctuary it was. 'I'd like to catch that
one!' cried Petros and off he ran, still chasing it
even after it had disappeared into the low undergrowth of poppies and wild herbs. Judith and
Alexis watched him stop to talk to another boy of
about his own age who had also strayed from the
adults who were with him.

'Leave him,' said Alexis before Judith could
call out for Petros to come back. 'He'll take no
harm. It isn't as if there's any likelihood of his
getting lost.'

However, both boys followed in their wake
when eventually they moved on, and as Judith
glanced back and noticed a young couple saun-
tering along behind the children, she guessed
that these were the parents of the little boy who
was chattering away to Petros, a boy who was
obviously an American.

Judith said, 'Isn't it surprising how many Americans come to Greece for their holidays?'

'They are usually in Greece as part of a tour of Europe.'

'They take such *long* holidays.'

'I know. It's been a puzzle to a lot of people for a long time.'

'Perhaps they are combining business with pleasure,' suggested Judith after a pause.

'Or perhaps they save for several years instead of taking short breaks every year as you do.'

'It's a good idea to save for several years and then be able to take two or three months off at once.'

He glanced at her with a faintly amused expression on his face. 'You English can't bear to be away from your cosy little nests for much longer than a couple of weeks.' Faintly derisive the tone which had the instant effect of bringing Judith's chin lifting and bringing a militant sparkle to her eyes.

'You speak as if we're namby-pambies!'

'Aren't you?'

'Not more than most.'

'An Englishman's home is his castle,' quoted Alexis, the words flicking out in an amused drawl. 'That's known the world over.'

'Is there anything wrong with being attached to one's home?' she demanded tartly.

'Nothing that I know of.'

'Then why are you sneering at us?'

'How sensitive you are.' The mild complaint in his voice was overshadowed by his half-amused, half-mocking expression. 'I absolutely refuse to be drawn into a battle of words with you, Judith,' he added when she did not speak.

She decided to remain silent, and gave her attention to far more interesting things than an exchange of counter strokes with a man who always managed to emerge the victor. In the various ruins there was more than enough to hold the attention of the average dilettante like herself and, as Alexis seemed to be keeping an eye on Petros, she wandered away to follow a different path, ears alert in case he should call her back.

But he let her go; she mingled with a group who had a guide with them, and so found herself learning far more than she would have done had she been relying solely on the booklet she had, and what she had previously read. She followed the group and listened avidly to all that was said as they went from monument to monument, seeing the House of the Dolphins and the House of the Masks, both exhibiting exquisite floor mosaics. Another was the House of the Trident, with two lions and two bulls on its columns, and the house which was clearly the home of a patrician couple called Cleopatra and Dioscourides. There was the Theatre, with its five thousand seats facing the sea. Marble baths, chairs, and tables were more than enough to give Judith a vivid picture of the highly civilised population of Roman times. All this was of course the ancient city which had occupied the slopes of Mount Cynthus, from the top of which could be enjoyed the magnificent view of the circle of the Cyclades Islands: Mykonos and Syros, Naxos, and Paros and Tinos, all floating on the cerulean sea like the shapes of long-dead sea monsters.

But of course it was the Greek remains that Judith was most interested in, and she left the tourists to hurry back, her eyes searching until she saw Alexis with Petros trotting contentedly beside him.

'I'm sorry,' she began, only now feeling guilty. 'I wanted to learn something—'

'Don't be so embarrassed,' broke in Alexis with a sudden frown. 'Nor is there any need for an apology. You're not tied to Petros and me, you know.'

She blushed. She still felt guilty, more so than before, perhaps. 'Which way are we going now?' she asked, biting her lip as she realised that they had probably already been to all that was interesting and would now want to explore the area to which she had already been. But Alexis said they had in fact been sitting down almost since the moment she had left them.

'The couple who had that little boy sat down and the two children were playing, so I thought I might as well let them carry on and enjoy themselves.'

She looked up at him. 'Are you bored?' She had no idea what made her ask the question and, it seemed, neither did he, because his straight dark brows instantly shot up in a gesture of enquiry.

'What makes you ask a question like that?' he wanted to know. 'Of course I'm not bored—' He spread a hand comprehensively. 'Only a moron could be bored in a place like this.'

Reassured, she smilingly asked again which way they were going.

'I suggest we wander along this way,' he answered. Then he added with a trace of anxiety, 'I'm wondering if this little chap's had enough. There isn't much here for a child of his age.'

'What shall we do, then? There's a café—so it says here in the book.' She looked down at Petros, who was bent low picking wildflowers. 'Are you hungry, or thirsty?'

'Not very. I want to see the lions. I heard a man say there were five and they were white. I've never seen white lions. Have you, Judith?'

'They're stone lions,' intervened Alexis, and the little boy's face dropped.

'Well,' he said after a pause, 'we can go and see them all the same.'

They were of course the island's most beautiful monuments—five remaining lions from the original sixteen which, made from the lovely Naxian marble, had guarded a sanctuary and the Sacred Lake which had witnessed the birth of Leto's children. The lake was now dried up, but it did not require much imagination on Judith's part to visualise the glory of its shining waters, fed as it was from the only river on the island, Inopos, also now dried up. There would have been swans and water flowers, she mused, a wistful smile hovering on her lips.

'You're a long way off.' The murmured words brought her face up and her smile deepened.

'A long way *back*,' she corrected.

'To Leto's day, I suppose,' with a shade of amusement in his voice. 'What a dreamer you are, Judith.' He paused a moment, and when he spoke again she felt sure it was on impulse.

'Greece fascinates you, so you ought to consider making your home here.'

'Alone?' She lifted her eyebrows. 'I daresay I shall come back for many holidays throughout my life, but to live here—' She shook her head and sighed. 'Greece is wonderful . . . but I can never live here.' Once, she thought, she had truly believed that her home was to be in Greece, in incredibly beautiful Delphi, where her future husband lived.

Alexis was frowning; he turned, then walked away, taking Petros with him and guiding him close to one of the lions. Judith, standing alone, watched him with the child, saw him bend down to Petros' level—or just above it, saw him pointing something out as he talked to the child, obviously explaining with infinite patience. Petros was absorbed, asking questions and then listening intently to the answers. Judith felt suddenly full up, emotionally affected, because she was even yet again remembering that she and Alexis had once been engaged. He would make a wonderful father. . . . He straightened up and patted the little boy's head. Petros tucked his hand into that of his uncle and they both returned to where Judith was standing.

'Petros is ready for those refreshments you mentioned,' said Alexis. 'Let us go over to the Tourist Pavilion and see what they have for lunch, shall we?'

The following evening they attended the captain's private cocktail party, given in his quarters. About twenty-five people had been invited and these naturally included those who shared his table, this being traditional on all cruises. Others invited included a millionaire wine producer and his wife, a wealthy Greek shipowner, and an hotel owner, all of whom had become known to Alexis and Judith during various social activities on the cruise. And now Judith seemed to be claimed by Adonys Pavlos, the hotel owner who was cruising on his own, having been advised by his doctor to take a rest. He was in his early thirties, dark and handsome and very confident of himself and—Judith soon realised—his prowess as a womaniser. His tactics amused her and she sparred with him verbally. This naturally brought laughter often because it was all a good-natured slanging match.

But without warning Judith was aware of that spine-prickling sensation that denoted something unpleasant, and at almost the same moment she heard her companion say, a flicker of humour in his voice, 'Your employer's expression's far from pleasant; it would seem that he doesn't approve of your giving me all this attention.' Adonys stared at her curiously as he spoke, and on the instant she knew he was pondering the possibility of her being Alexis' pillow-friend.

She turned slowly, to meet the almost hostile gaze of the man whose attention she would far rather have than that of this lady-killer, charming though his manner might be. Alexis held her eyes as a predator holds its prey—there was no obvious anger now, just a prolonged scrutiny, cold and piercing, and she went red beneath it. Anger was the spur which made her turn her back on him, but even then she felt his eyes burning into her.

Carelessly she sipped her drink, deliberately giving all her attention to Adonys again.

'You're not worried, obviously,' he remarked, his strongly accented voice now grating a little on her ears. 'Of course, if he's only your employer, then he has no right to object to your behaviour.'

'"If"?' she repeated, ignoring the rest. 'He *is* my employer—and *nothing* else.'

'Funny situation, though,' Adonys murmured, his eyes directed over her shoulder to where Alexis was standing. 'A man doesn't usually have charge of a small child like Petros.' There was a question in the words which Judith chose to ignore. Adonys waited a moment to see if she would vouchsafe some information. Then, with a resigned shrug of his shoulders, he began flirting with her again. She laughed at some remark he made and hoped Alexis could hear.

'You're an unusual type,' Adonys was saying. 'Do you always pass flattery off by laughing at the man who praises your beauty?'

'It depends on the reason for the flattery,' she returned, eyes dancing. 'You, like most men, are an opportunist.'

He laughed and said banteringly, 'I rather think I'd have very little opportunity with you.'

'So right you are!'

Again he laughed, his eyes travelling over her shoulder as before. 'Why aren't you married? A lovely girl like you ought not to be wasting her life and her attractions by serving as a nanny.'

'I enjoy my job,' was all she answered to that.

'It certainly gives you a few perks. Do you often come on trips like this?'

'This is the first.' She was becoming bored with Adonys, especially with the way he looked at her . . . stripping her with sensuous exploration in his dark Greek eyes.

'I think we had better move round and socialise,' she suggested. 'We're not contributing to the success of the party.'

'I'm satisfied,' he began, then stopped as Alexis approached. *'Yassoo!'* Adonys said boldly, and defiantly, eyes challenging.

Judith knew he was thoroughly enjoying the situation. What she could not understand was Alexis' obvious objection to her chatting with Adonys—for, judging from his expression at this moment, he was plainly suppressing anger. To say he was formidable was putting it mildly, she thought, aware of the highly charged atmosphere. She stared up at him. The fine bones of his face were rigid, his eyes hard as steel.

'Judith,' he said very quietly, 'don't you think you should contribute to the success of the captain's party by moving about a little? It's usual, you know—and obligatory.'

Her colour deepened, burning in her cheeks, for Alexis had actually admonished her, and at the same time implied that she was ignorant of the rules of polite behaviour.

However, anything she had to say to him must be kept for another time. She smiled disarmingly and said with an edge of apology in her tone, 'Of course, Alexis. I was just going to, as a matter of fact.'

'Must you?' from Adonys blatantly. 'We were just beginning to enjoy ourselves,' he said to Alexis. 'You're a spoilsport, old chap. Leave Judith where she is. . . .' His voice trailed off to silence as he caught Judith's expression. He shrugged. 'Oh, well, he *is* your employer—so you say—and, therefore, you have to do as he bids you.' And with that Adonys swung away, to find another target.

Chatter was going on all round, but between Judith and Alexis the silence was thick and heavy. She was not only feeling the sting of Alexis' recent reproof, but also that of Adonys' swaggering insolence. As a result her own temper had risen and the blood seemed to be boiling in her cheeks even before Alexis, his voice stiff with fury, said quietly, so that no one else would hear, 'Your behaviour just now was shameless. Even if you have no *self*-esteem, you might at least have consideration for me! Everyone was looking at you—'

'Nonsense!' she interjected hotly. 'It was only you! Other people are fully occupied with one another, so why should they be giving particular attention to Adonys and me?'

'You were so absorbed that you didn't even notice anyone else in the room, but they were noticing you!'

Suddenly she was bewildered by the sheer magnitude of his anger. It seemed totally out of proportion since, after all, she had only been sparring with Adonys. Had she laughed too loudly? she wondered. Had it seemed like flirting? Most people on board knew by now that Adonys was a womaniser, and jokes had been made about the girls he chatted up, with speculations as to which of their staterooms he visited. Judith bit her lip, seeing her innocent little escapade in an altogether different light now. But self-blame did nothing to tone down her temper; on the contrary, it served to increase it simply because she was now angry with herself, as well as both Alexis and Adonys.

Her thoughts returning to the disproportionate measure of Alexis' anger, she asked curiously, managing to hold her own anger in check only with the greatest difficulty, 'Perhaps you will explain just why you've taken such exception to my talking to Adonys. After all, my friends have nothing to do with you.'

'Friends!' he gritted, eyes glinting. 'Did you say *friend!*'

Judith's teeth clamped together. Anger let loose brought a huskiness to her voice, but at least she managed to keep her tone low. 'I did not say *pillow*-friend!' she threw at him, fully aware she was worsening the situation, but, held in the grip of wrath as she was, she spoke wildly and without a care for the damage she might be doing. 'Get this, Alexis—if I want to have Adonys for a friend, then it has nothing to do with you, so keep out of my private affairs!' This whispering was trying to her nerves, she realised, for her instinct was to raise her voice in order to emphasise her words. 'I shall not allow you to dictate to me. . . .' Her voice trailed off and the warm colour of humiliation flooded into her cheeks.

Alexis, his eyes hard and cold with dislike, had turned about and left her standing there, glass in hand.

She glanced round as she reached the dinner table, then breathed a deep sigh of relief when she was greeted with smiles. She had half-expected to find herself facing curious eyes, or even censorious ones.

Alexis was the only one without a welcoming smile, and she averted her head, unwilling to look upon the smooth mask of his face or those partly sheathed eyes which she knew would hold dislike.

The captain arrived a few moments later and the meal could then begin, for although it was not necessary to await his appearance, a delay was usually made out of courtesy if it was definitely known that he meant to join them for dinner. If the ship was leaving a port he would not appear, and sometimes he had his dinner in the quiet and peace of his quarters.

Tonight his charming smile embraced everyone as he said he hoped they had enjoyed his party.

'It was lovely!' from Ruth with her customary vivacious eagerness. 'So many nice people are on this ship, Captain.'

'We're rather fortunate on this particular line,' he said with a swift sideways glance at Alexis. 'We seem to attract nice people.'

The conversation became light and inconsequential, and when the meal was over the captain left them, so that they were not privileged on this particular evening by having the best view of the floor show. Alexis could of course have had a reserved table, but he had not bothered to avail himself of the privilege, since he had no wish that passengers should show curiosity as to who he was.

'Are you two coming to see the show?' asked Ed as they all trooped from the restaurant together.

Alexis shook his head, and when he spoke he set Judith's hackles rising by speaking for her, as well as himself. 'We're going out on deck for a while. It's cooler and fresher out there.'

Judith flashed him a glance but made no demur when he manoeuvred her towards the wide, thickly carpeted stairway from which they could eventually reach the sun-deck.

'I didn't particularly want to come out here,' she began once they had arrived.

'I want to talk to you.' There was still a residue of anger in his voice and manner, but no sign of the cold rage which he had with difficulty been suppressing at the party. 'I want to impress on you that there'll be no flirting while you're on the trip, either with Adonys or anyone else. Do I make myself clear?'

'Perfectly clear,' she replied in icy tones. 'But now let me speak,' she added after swallowing to rid her throat of the little ball of anger which had settled there. 'I please myself with what I do in my leisure time, and if I want to flirt, as you call it, then I shall do just that.'

They were standing by the rail but facing one another, attitudes challenging as if they were ready to do battle. Alexis looked at her with a glowering expression and his mouth was tight.

'Perhaps,' he said, 'I had better assert my authority as your employer . . . and curtail your leisure time.'

She gave a start. He had effectively deflated her already. 'What do you mean?'

'Only that you are having far more time off than a nanny ought to. On a trip like this an employee in your capacity would be required to stay with her charge in the evenings.'

An employee. . . . Although she had accepted that she was his employee, she had never expected him to refer to her as such. She said chokingly, 'If that is what you want, then I have no alternative other than to regard your instructions.'

'I haven't yet instructed you to stay with Petros.' He turned from her impatiently and placed his hands upon the rail. Judith looked at the clear, finely etched profile and swallowed convulsively as into her mind came an essence of recollection and she remembered so profoundly just how much she had loved him, admired him . . . worshipped him, almost.

'Are you going to instruct me to stay with Petros?' she asked at last to break the oppressive silence. She noticed the tightened muscles of his neck, the implacable sternness of his jaw, and as her eyes fell to his hands she saw that the knuckle bones were gleaming white beneath the teak darkness of his skin. 'Are you?' she repeated when he did not immediately answer.

'I might,' he said through his teeth as he turned to give her a cold stare.

'You seem to be making an issue out of something relatively unimportant,' she commented. 'Your anger was out of all proportion, so much so that it puzzled me.' To her surprise his eyes took on a closed expression—almost as if she had caught him unawares. She frowned bewilderedly, unable to understand why that sort of idea should have occurred to her.

'I'll give you my decision tomorrow as to whether or not you're to stay with Petros,' was all he said. Then, swinging round on his heel, he bade her good night over his shoulder and disappeared down the steps.

Chapter Eight

Judith and Petros were already having breakfast when Alexis appeared. As there were no rules for keeping to one table for breakfast, Judith had chosen to sit near a window. Alexis stood glancing round until his eyes found them. Then he strode over with that lithe gait which seemed in itself to set him apart, give him that air of superiority which for Judith was so much a part of his attraction. Noble he looked, as he covered the distance with his long, easy strides. But his face was set in dark, forbidding lines, and Judith's heart sank right into her feet. Foolishly—and optimistically—she had believed that his ill humour would have evaporated during the night and that he would have awakened to find himself admitting that he had been much too severe with her.

'I'm having cereal and honey,' Petros informed Alexis as he sat down. 'Francesco is serving us and he gave me honey and jam and marmalade to choose from!'

'And you've chosen honey. Good boy.' Alexis looked across the table to bid Judith good morning.

She returned the greeting. Then for the first time since she had learnt that Camille was to join the ship, she mentioned her. She supposed it was because the girl had constantly been in

165

the background of her mind for the past twenty-four hours.

'Miss Longman will be with us tomorrow, you said—when we arrive at Rhodes?'

The dark Greek eyes took on a guarded look. 'She will be joining us, yes.' A slight pause. Then with a curious inflection, 'Have you any particular reason for broaching the subject of Camille?'

Judith averted her head, for she had to conceal the jealousy in her eyes. 'Not really,' she answered with assumed carelessness. 'It was just a passing comment, that's all.'

Alexis passed her the toast, an action deliberately intended to bring her head up again.

'Thank you.' She lifted her face, but looked at him through flickering lashes.

'Something's troubling you,' he said perceptively. 'What is it?'

She hesitated, fully aware that he had guessed she was not happy at the idea of Camille's joining them. Resignedly she said, 'It won't be quite the same. . . .' And then she trailed off, vexed with herself for saying a thing like that. It was out of place and she added swiftly before he could speak, 'I'm sorry. It has nothing to do with me. I suppose I was thinking that my position would become that of nanny.'

'Hasn't it been that up till now?'

Frowningly, she replied, 'Not entirely. I mean, I've dined with you and danced—and gone about with you when—when we've been ashore.' She looked at him and wished it were possible to go back a moment ago, before she had mentioned Camille.

'You will still dine with me—with us,' he corrected, the most odd expression in his eyes as he stared at Judith's bent head. 'As for going ashore—well, there's only one place left after Rhodes, as you know.'

She nodded. Crete, island of the *Vendetta* and of marvellous Knossos, where the Minoan Palace had been excavated to reveal many of its original eight hundred rooms, excavated mainly at the expense of Sir Arthur Evans, whose heart was buried there after he had spent thirty years of his life, and his entire fortune, on the project which gave him so much satisfaction. And to others? The joy of roaming the site of the Palace, the pleasure of re-living in imagination the splendour of the Minoan era, when King Minos ruled supreme. Wonderful frescoes had been unearthed after being buried beneath the innocent-looking hill on which sheep had grazed since time unremembered. An innocent hill . . . but when seen by Evans it became an exciting mystery he set himself to solve. Judith had been considering the visit to Knossos as the highlight of the cruise. Although she had known that Camille would be there, too, it was not until now that the girl became real, now when she was to join the ship within hours.

As there was to be a full day at sea, several sporting activities had been arranged for the entertainment of the passengers. Judith and Petros watched while Alexis took part in a clay-pigeon shooting match, with Petros dancing up and down every time his uncle shattered one of the saucer-shaped pieces of clay. After lunch there were special games for the children. There were supervisors provided by the shipping company, so Judith and Alexis were free to join in the quoits contest, after which they took a swim, then lazed on deck, stretched out on loungers while white-coated stewards went round with trays containing ice-cold drinks.

Later, Judith spent over two hours with Petros before bathing him and putting him to bed. He went off to sleep within seconds, literally having drifted away as his head touched the pillow. Standing there for a few quiet moments looking down at the chubby features so innocently relaxed, Judith wondered how Helen could even have thought of leaving him. Surely she was missing him. At present Petros was not missing her, simply because there was so much to occupy his mind—but once they were home again? A sigh escaped her and sadness brought shadows to her eyes, shadows that were still there when she joined Alexis in the lounge for an aperitif before dinner.

'Something wrong?' he was swift to ask, his eyes intensely scrutinising her face.

'It's Petros,' she explained. 'He's happy now, but what about when he gets back to the villa? He's going to be asking for his parents.'

'Yes, I know.' Alexis' words were clipped. 'I ought to do something about finding Helen. Mother's obviously worried out of her mind, even though she's trying not to show it too much in case she upsets other members of the family.'

'I wish I'd met your mother,' murmured Judith without knowing why.

'Perhaps you will,' he returned. 'She'll be coming up to the villa for a meal when we get back.'

* * *

Camille was on the quayside at Acandia when the *Santa Maura* glided gracefully in. The girl was all smiles until she spotted Judith and Petros. Then her face underwent a dramatic change. Judith watched as Alexis took both her hands, watched his profile and then his eyes for some sign of expression that would provide her with a clue to his feelings. His face seemed to be a mask, devoid of emotion to the lengths of indifference.

'Oh, but it's good to see you!' gushed Camille, deliberately ignoring Judith. 'Have you had a wonderful time? Oh, but how I wished I could have been with you from the beginning!'

'It's been exceedingly pleasant,' Alexis answered. Then he spread a hand towards where Judith was standing, just a few feet away, with Petros now clinging to her skirt.

'Camille . . . Judith—you two have met, of course.'

'Briefly,' from Camille. She regarded Judith with a sort of casual indifference which set her teeth on edge. 'Is the little boy enjoying himself?' She smiled thinly down at him. 'Have you been bored, dear?'

'*Ochi.*'

Camille's mouth went tight. But because she was aware of being watched by Alexis, she managed to produce a smile as she said, 'You haven't? But what have you been doing?'

'There are activities for the children,' Alexis put in shortly.

Camille moved closer to him, fluttered him a glance from under her long, curling lashes as she slipped an arm through his and said purringly, 'Well, darling, what are we doing? Have you any plans?' And without affording him the chance to answer, she turned to Judith and said, 'You'll be taking your young charge onto the sands, I expect?'

Judith's mouth went tight. 'Of course,' she answered. 'Come on, Petros; we'll buy a bucket and spade.' Angry and somehow humiliated, she gave Alexis a swift look. Before he had time to speak she was walking away, setting a pace that necessitated Petros' having to run to keep up with her.

'Judith!'

She heard Alexis' call but ignored it. A taxi was standing by and on impulse she wrenched open the door and ushered Petros inside, following swiftly. 'The Miramare Beach,' she instructed.

'Very good hotel, no?'

'I've never been there,' she answered. 'But I've been told the beach is very nice.'

'Very good for children!'

'Judith, are you angry?' asked Petros sometime later when, having bought a small bucket and spade, he and Judith were on the sands.

'No, of course not.' She managed to smile. 'Why do you ask a thing like that?'

'You look angry,' he said.

She bit her lip, feeling contrite at the idea of making the little boy anxious. And she resolutely threw off her dejection and gave herself up to helping Petros enjoy himself, which he did. Then they went into the hotel for cool drinks and ice cream.

But all the time there was a nagging worry and anxiety at the back of Judith's mind. She knew she ought not to have run off in the taxi like that; yet on the other hand, try as she would, she could not imagine the four of them spending the day happily together. Not only would she herself have felt uncomfortable, but Petros would not have found much enjoyment, either.

'Are we going back to the ship now?' Petros was asking, having finished his refreshments and becoming restless.

'Are you tired?'

'A bit, but not much.' He came to her and took hold of her hand. 'I want to go back because there isn't anything to do now.'

She nodded her head, drained her glass, and rose to her feet. 'Very well, we'll go back.'

Once on board she took him to their suite and rang for a steward to bring Petros' tea.

'Aren't you having any?' he asked Judith.

'I'm not very hungry, but I'll have one of these nice sandwiches.' She was still troubled inwardly, uncertain as to whether she ought to seek out Alexis before dinner or just arrive at the table. She knew that an extra place was to be arranged; she knew also that Ruth, for one, was going to be intensely curious about the glamourous new arrival, especially when she was introduced by Alexis as his friend.

Her actions were almost mechanical as, after seeing Petros to bed and reading to him until his eyes closed and he drifted off to sleep, she took a shower and began to dress for dinner. It was not to be a formal evening, so she chose a flared summer skirt in flower-printed cotton, the background yellow, the leaves a gentle shade of green to enhance the crimson poppies and the blue forget-me-nots. The blouse was white, high at the throat and tied with thin black ribbon. She stared at her reflection, frowned at the picture of a girl looking much younger than her age, then turned with a resigned shrug and picked up the small white leather bag in which she had put her comb and handkerchief.

After another glance at Petros, followed by a phone call to the minder service to say she was leaving the child, she went along to the stairs and made her way slowly to the dining room.

The only people at the table were Ruth and Ed, and Gloria, pale and unsmiling, her attention on the menu she held in her hand.

'All alone?' from Ruth. 'I thought you always had a drink with Alexis before dinner.'

'He's—er—with a friend. He did tell you someone was joining us at Rhodes.'

'Ah! Yes, I remember!' Ruth's eyes were alight with curiosity. 'What is he like?'

'It's a lady.' Judith smiled up at Mario as he handed her a menu.

'A lady?' repeated Ed, undoubtedly surprised.

Gloria lifted her face and looked at Judith, who swallowed convulsively as she wondered what to say. But there seemed to be only one thing to say. 'It's his girl friend, Miss Longman —Camille,' she thought to add, since everyone had from the first used given names.

'Oh. . . .'

The one short word spoke volumes. Judith wished she could disappear. But more than ever she wished she had not come quite so early. It would have been less embarrassing if she had arrived after Alexis and Camille had sat down.

'The captain won't be with us this evening.' Gloria spoke as if she felt the urge to come to Judith's rescue and change the subject. 'He'll be getting the ship out of port in a few minutes.' She glanced at her watch. 'We sail at half past eight, I believe?'

Judith looked gratefully at her. 'Yes, that's right.'

'Did you have a good day?'

'It was most pleasant, yes. Petros and I spent several hours on the sands.' Judith threw her a smile. 'Did you have a good day?'

'Gloria came with us,' intervened Ed. 'We all went up to Lindos.'

'We went by donkey to the Acropolis; it was very interesting, and the view was quite exceptional—right down to the deep blue harbour where Saint Paul landed almost two thousand years ago.'

Ruth looked up and Judith knew by her expression that Alexis and Camille had arrived, but she did not look round. She waited until they were seated before lifting her eyes to meet the narrowed ones of her employer. He made the introductions. Camille, intent on charming the group sitting there, produced a winning smile which was reflected in the vivid blue of her eyes.

'It's nice to meet you,' said Ruth with flickering glances at Alexis and Judith. 'You met the ship on its arrival?'

'Yes. It's a lovely vessel, and the sight of it coming into port was most impressive.' She added that she and Alexis had had a most enjoyable day.

Alexis, as he accepted the menu from Mario, looked at Judith and said unsmilingly, 'What did you do all day, Judith?'

'We spent most of the time on the sands. Petros loved it.' Her voice was cool, for she had gathered her composure, much to her surprise, since Camille's words had informed everyone that she and Alexis had gone off together. 'Where did you get to?' she was able to say in the same calm way.

'We went to the Old City,' from Camille, casting Judith a cursory glance and then turning away, towards Ruth and Ed, who was sitting beside her. 'The Knights' Palace is so fascinating—I suppose one should refer to it as the Grand Master's Palace,' she amended with a smile. There was a purring quality about her voice which set Judith's teeth on edge. 'The famous Street of the Knights is so fascinating, too, with the influence of their various countries to be seen in the buildings.'

'Their magnificent houses? Yes, I agree that the Norman and Tudor and Venetian influences make for a most interesting variety.' Ed nodded as he spoke and went on before anyone could comment: 'I've been to Rhodes before, several years ago. I, too, found the Old Quarter most intriguing.' He turned his head to look at Judith. 'You didn't do any sight-seeing, then?'

'No—I have a job to do, Ed, which is looking after Petros. At Rhodes there was a lovely beach he could play on. He'd not have been interested in the things you and Miss Longman are talking about.' Judith managed to keep her voice steady in spite of the dejection possessing her. She was profoundly conscious of Ruth's eyes upon her, and more profoundly conscious of the enigmatic stare of her employer.

'Pity, though, that you didn't see something of the old part of the town, for I imagine you are one of those people who really appreciates the past and its fascinating history.'

'Yes, indeed. Stories of the Crusades held me from the time I was very young.'

'It's amazing how many people just look, but take nothing in as regards the aesthetic values of what they are seeing.'

Judith nodded in agreement. 'So many people draw a self-created veil between them and the idyllic world of the fantasy of one's imagination.' She caught Alexis' eyes, saw their expression of interest before it became shuttered.

'Aren't we getting rather deep?' Camille's voice was edged with a sneering quality matched by the look she threw at Judith. Amusement came through as well when she added, 'You appear to take things very seriously, Miss Sommerville.'

'Which can't be bad,' from Ruth brightly. 'There's a lack of seriousness in this frivolous world of ours.'

Alexis shot her a look of surprise, since Ruth herself always appeared to be of the frivolous type.

'I'm sure you are right,' he said in his finely timbred voice.

Camille coloured slightly. Then, in a sort of retaliating mood, she began to talk to Ed again about the three ancient sites of Rhodes, one of which was, of course, Lindos. But Judith was interested in the other two, Ialysus and Camirus, both of which seemed to offer endless inter-

est to anyone keen on archaeology. Judith realised she had missed the best of Rhodes, but
consoled herself with the knowledge that her
young charge had had a very happy day.

After dinner she made an immediate excuse to
get away. She avoided the curious eyes of Ruth
and the sympathetic ones of Gloria, and even
avoided a direct look at Alexis as she said, 'It's
been a tiring day, so I think I'll go to my stateroom and read, then turn in early. Good night,
all.' She was gone even as they answered, moving the length of the dining-room rapidly, nerves
tingling in case Alexis should come after her.
Yet why should he? she was soon asking herself.
He had Camille now. . . .

Judith had changed from her dinner clothes
and put on a dainty midnight-blue leisure gown
when with a sudden frown she stared at the
door. Someone was knocking, and in what could
only be described as an imperious way. She was
not surprised when she opened the door and saw
who her caller was.

'Hello—er—what do you want?'

Alexis was already in and kicking the door to
behind him. 'What was the idea of disappear-
ing immediately after dinner was over?' he demanded, leaning on the door with his arms
folded.

'It was the proper thing to do.'

'Indeed? Perhaps you'll explain why.'

She drew an impatient breath. 'You must
have known I felt unwanted—the intruder.
After all, I'm only the nanny to your nephew.
You once referred to me yourself as your employee.' Pale of countenance but hopeful of re-
taining her composure, she looked at him with

head held high and an expression of assumed unfriendliness in her eyes. 'I can't think why you have come here, Alexis, but as you can see, I'm about to go to bed.'

His fine mouth compressed as the dark eyes narrowed into anger. 'This morning,' he said through his teeth. 'What reason had you for clearing off like that in a taxi?'

'For the same reason—I felt unwanted.' She stared at him challengingly. 'Can you imagine the four of us spending a pleasant, friendly day together?'

'You don't like Camille, do you?' An unfathomable quality seemed to overscore his anger. He was regarding her with an odd expression.

'I have no interest in her.'

A low laugh escaped him. 'I believe you have a most natural interest in her,' he asserted, and her eyes flew open.

'If you're hinting at jealousy, Alexis—'

'Not merely hinting,' he interrupted smoothly, that odd expression still in his eyes.

'Then it's just another manifestation of your innate self-esteem, your pompous assumption that your attractions are infallible—' She stopped at the raising of his finger. His eyes were glinting now and she took an involuntary step backwards.

'I haven't come here to listen to your insults, Judith.'

'Then what did you come for?' Tears were close. Although she was adopting this manner of enmity, her heart was treacherously at variance with her mind and its determination not to let him see how much she was being hurt. For the tears were coming right up from her heart, tears

177

she knew she could not hold back much longer. She heard herself say huskily, 'Please go, Alexis. I really do want to go to bed.'

He left his position by the door and instinctively she backed away, all too aware of just how little space she could put between him and herself.

'You've not shown this—er—tiredness before.' Alexis' voice as was as sceptical as the look he gave her.

'Today was different.'

'Because of Camille?'

'Because of the hours spent on the sands, in the sun, playing with Petros.' The tears were forming a cloud behind her eyes, a cloud that would not hold them much longer. 'I asked you to go. . . .' Almost angrily she lifted a hand to touch lashes already moist. 'Go away!' she cried. 'Get out of here! Your girl friend will be waiting— Oh, leave me alone!' But it was too late; he had his steel-strong arms about her, tightening their hold as she began to struggle. 'Get away from me!' she fumed as he tried to kiss her.

'You little wildcat!' She had tried to bite him and he gripped her chin just in time. Forcing it up with a grip of steel, he compelled her to look at him. 'If you'd managed to succeed in that little attempt, my girl, you'd be across my knee at this moment, begging for mercy!'

His mouth came down in ruthless reprisal for her abortive attack, his lips forcing hers apart for the incursion of his tongue, his hands moving to her back, leaving a trail of heat as they slid, very slowly, right down to where the long, lean fingers could shape themselves to the soft, pliant flesh of her curves.

She quivered in every nerve and cell in her body, quivered against the insistent male hardness of him. The overwhelming instinct to free her hands and wind them round his neck was so strong that it took all her determination not to do so.

'Stop resisting me!' he ordered. At this moment he was all Greek, arrogantly demanding, masterfully expecting immediate obedience. Instead of obeying him, Judith began renewed struggles, twisting her face away from his, wrenching her body in desperate, sideways movements. But she was fast losing strength, and her breathing was laboured so that she had to open her mouth in search of air. Alexis, seizing the opportunity, crushed her lips, keeping them apart as he took his fill of their sweetness.

Her senses reeled; she had to cling to him in her weakness, could offer no resistance when his hand found a dainty ribbon bow which formed the embellishment that covered the metal top of the zipper which ran the full length of her gown. Alexis had both her wrists imprisoned in one of his hands behind her back; the zipper slid easily to below her waist. She cried out in protest as the gown was removed from one shoulder and then the other. He released her hands but she was too exhausted for physical combat. Resignedly, she stared, swallowing convulsively, as the gown swirled down and came to rest in a circle about her feet. She lifted her face, lips trembling, tears bright on her lashes.

'I h-hope,' she whispered brokenly, 'th-that this is going to give you—you satisfaction. . . .'

Silence, profound and long as their eyes held—those of the arrogant conqueror, and those of the vanquished.

'Judith. . . .' It seemed an eternity before the emotional silence was broken, and then so softly that she could scarcely hear the one huskily spoken word.

'Have you th-thought of—of afterwards? Don't you care that you're—you're letting Camille down?' Judith lifted a trembling hand to stem a tear, blinking rapidly at the same time.

'Judith.' The word came again, but in a stronger voice this time. 'My dear. . . .' The change in his expression was so dramatic that she gave a little gasp, her eyes widening in bewilderment. 'Oh, my love, what was I intending doing to you?' He shook his head and she saw a nerve throbbing out of control in his throat. He could obviously feel its wild pulsation, for he pressed a disbelieving finger against it.

Judith's lips moved but no words came. Automatically she looked down again to the gown at her feet; only now was she fully aware of being nearly naked, for the filmy, diaphanous nightgown hid nothing, and it was very short into the bargain. But Alexis was not looking at her body, only into her eyes, which were fast losing their stricken expression. She found to her amazement that she wanted to smile at him, but her lips were still too stiff. She was aware, too, of a pouding in her head as with the lengthening silence her emotions became tumultuous, and eventually it was Alexis who smiled, a smile that seemed to be a compound of tenderness and regret.

He had moved a little distance from her. Driven by some impulse she could not control, Judith made a spontaneous gesture, extending her hands. He took them, enclosing them tenderly before bringing one to his lips.

Judith swallowed over and over again, still trying to speak, to ask the question which she knew full well was superfluous. But eventually she managed to smile and to ask, 'You . . . care?'

He nodded, and she realised with a little shock that the reason for the drawn-out silence was because he was as emotionally affected as she was.

'Yes, dearest,' he answered simply, 'I care.'

'Camille?' She had to say it, as if instinct—a primitively jealous instinct—was forcing her to get the girl out of the way once and for all.

Alexis smiled with faint humour and understanding as he replied, taking her in his arms and gently tilting her face. 'She never meant very much to me at all.'

A small pause. Then, again driven by something primitive, 'She was your pillow-friend?'

'Must you ask that, darling?'

She shook her head. He had answered her, in the affirmative, but she understood his reluctance to cast a stain unnecessarily on Camille's name.

'Alexis, when you came here . . . did you really mean to—to hurt me?' Her lovely face, pale but totally composed and free from strain, was lifted to his.

'Would it have hurt you?' he countered gently, a hand touching her throat.

'Perhaps not physically,' she had to admit. 'But mentally—yes, it would.' She paused a moment. 'It would have been a dishonourable act, and I've always believed you to be an honourable man, Alexis.' Simple words, spoken like a child whose trust is strong and sincere. With an almost rough gesture which belied the tenderness in his eyes, Alexis brought her body close, his lips seeking hers in a kiss that was as cruel as it was tender.

'My beloved,' he said after a long while, during which he practised astonishing self-control, merely caressing her hair and throat and shoulders, 'I've tried so hard to resist you—but now—' He held her away from him and his eyes held both tenderness and irony. 'Now, my dearest, you have won. I want you so much that I just have to ask you to be my wife.'

Judith shut her eyes as waves of joy flowed over her like a deluge of warm, tropical water from a coral sea. 'It's not just . . . desire?'

'It's not just desire, my love.' His gentle hands cupped her face. 'I was angry that you came, because believe it or not, I'd had the devil's own job in trying to forget you—'

'Then why did you try to forget me?' she asked logically. 'You could have come over to England, or given Helen a hint—'

'I *wanted* to forget you,' he broke in. 'You see, although I asked you to marry me, I didn't really want to give up my freedom. You knew at the time that it was desire which prompted my proposal—'

'Not at the time, Alexis,' she cut in to correct. 'It was later, if you remember.'

He nodded in recollection. 'Yes, dear, I do remember. However, as I was saying, I never wanted to give up my freedom, and the moment you arrived at the villa I knew you still held an attraction for me and I felt trapped, for I was sure that no amount of persuasion would make you my pillow-friend, and I feared I would again reach the point where I'd ask you to marry me.' Alexis stopped, to kiss her passionately on the lips, the temples, the throat, where the hollow curved down to meet her shoulder.

'So it was a sort of relief when you could find an excuse for jilting me. . . .' Judith stopped and frowned. She ought not to have said a thing like that, even if it had come perceptively into her head as he was speaking. To her relief he merely smiled ruefully and admitted that what she said was true.

'But now, my beloved, there is no longer any doubt in my mind. I love you,' he added simply, his dark eyes tender as they looked deeply into hers. His lips came close in a light caress; she clung to him, pressing close to feel the exciting warmth of him, to savour the pleasure-pain when in response he arched her body to shape it to the granite hardness of his thighs. She knew all the joy of those long-ago times, took in the musky male odour, pervasive, like the echo from an uncertain past.

'Is it true?' she whispered huskily when his lips left hers. 'Alexis, is it really true?'

'What must I do, my darling, to convince you?' He held her at arm's length so that he could slide loving eyes over her body. 'You tempt me to show you just how much—'

'I want my gown!' she broke in, panic seizing her.

Laughter was his answer as, lifting her as if she were a feather-weight, he deliberately kicked the gown away.

'Alexis. . . .'

'Darling, I shan't do anything you don't want me to.'

'My gown, then.'

He bent to pick it up, then put it back on her.

'Oh . . . thank you very much!'

'Silly child.' He drew her close, gown and all. 'But I love you for your ideals, my sweet.' Moments of bliss passed between them before Alexis said, as if memory had just nudged his mind. 'God, but I was jealous of that Leslie bloke, and then Adonys!'

'I did wonder about Leslie,' she admitted thoughtfully. But then went on to add, 'I daren't let myself believe you cared, though, Alexis, simply because it seemed it would be too good to be true.'

'Well, it was true, and if I hadn't refused to admit it, we'd be married now and you'd not be protecting your virtue with this—' He gave the gown a tug, then laughed and kissed her passionately.

'Why did Camille come today?' Judith asked curiously.

'It was arranged weeks ago. I didn't put her off because I was still trying to resist you, my love, and it seemed it would be easier if Camille was allowed to stay round.' He went on to add that, tomorrow, he would tell Camille that he and Judith were to be married.

'Let me kiss you again,' he said, abruptly changing the subject. 'And then I must go . . . before I blot my copybook with you again.'

Two weeks later they were standing together on the patio after dinner, having been married earlier in the village church. There would be a honeymoon later, but for now both wanted to be in their own home overlooking one of the most beautiful and dramatic scenes in all of Greece. Helen had taken Petros, because the man she was living with had made her do her duty as a mother. That she was glad to have him was patently clear. As for Petros—he had cried a little to be leaving his uncle and Judith, but judging by the way he snuggled into his mother's loving arms, it would seem that he knew just where he really wanted to be. What would be the outcome neither Alexis nor Judith would hazard a guess, but from Judith's point of view at least it seemed that the little boy would in the end be far happier with a man who wanted him than with a father who, from the first, had appeared to be indifferent to the needs of his son.

'Beloved, what are you thinking?'

'About Petros and Helen, and this man who sounds rather nice— Oh, I know you don't believe in divorce,' she added swiftly, 'but in this case, Alexis, I feel sure it is the best thing for everyone.'

'Perhaps you're right,' agreed after a pause.

'I shall have to send for my things,' she murmured presently as her thoughts wandered.

'How surprised everyone will be—Lena, in particular.'

'We might go over to England as part of our honeymoon,' Alexis promised, bringing her close and bending his head to kiss her eager lips. 'You're so beautiful. . . . Why should I be so lucky to have a second chance? It would have served me right if you'd found someone else.'

'It just wasn't to be, darling,' Judith returned. 'We were meant for each other. It was destiny.'

'I agree. Nevertheless, I was a fool to risk losing you.' And as if he would make sure she was his now, he crushed her body to him, taking her lips, exploring the sweet, dark secret of her mouth while possessively letting his warm hands roam over her curves, from her lovely young breasts to her waist and thighs . . . and lower.

She pressed to him, knew the pleasure and excitement of his rising desire and said huskily, and shyly, her face pressed against his shoulder, 'Let's go in, Alexis. . . .'

'Beloved. . . .' His lips found hers again in a long and tender kiss before, sweeping her into his arms, he carried her through the open French window into the house.

Silhouette ❦ *Romance*

15-Day Free Trial Offer
6 Silhouette Romances

6 Silhouette Romances, free for 15 days! We'll send you 6 new Silhouette Romances to keep for 15 days, absolutely free! If you decide not to keep them, send them back to us. You pay nothing.

Free Home Delivery. But if you enjoy them as much as we think you will, keep them by paying the invoice enclosed with your free trial shipment. We'll pay all shipping and handling charges. You get the convenience of Home Delivery and we pay the postage and handling charge each month.

Don't miss a copy. The Silhouette Book Club is the way to make sure you'll be able to receive every new romance we publish before they're sold out. There is no minimum number of books to buy and you can cancel at any time.

This offer expires October 31, 1982

Silhouette Book Club, Dept. SBO 17B
120 Brighton Road, Clifton, NJ 07012

Please send me 6 Silhouette Romances to keep for 15 days, absolutely free. I understand I am not obligated to join the Silhouette Book Club unless I decide to keep them.

NAME⎯⎯⎯⎯⎯⎯⎯⎯⎯⎯⎯⎯⎯⎯⎯⎯⎯⎯⎯⎯

ADDRESS⎯⎯⎯⎯⎯⎯⎯⎯⎯⎯⎯⎯⎯⎯⎯⎯⎯⎯

CITY⎯⎯⎯⎯⎯⎯⎯⎯⎯⎯STATE⎯⎯⎯⎯ZIP⎯⎯⎯⎯

Silhouette Romance

IT'S YOUR OWN SPECIAL TIME

Contemporary romances for today's women.
Each month, six very special love stories will be yours
from SILHOUETTE. Look for them wherever books are sold
or order now from the coupon below.

$1.50 each

Hampson	☐ 1	☐ 4	☐ 16	☐ 27	Browning	☐ 12	☐ 38	☐ 53	☐ 73
	☐ 28	☐ 40	☐ 52	☐ 64	☐ 94	☐ 93			
Stanford	☐ 6	☐ 25	☐ 35	☐ 46	Michaels	☐ 15	☐ 32	☐ 61	☐ 87
	☐ 58	☐ 88			John	☐ 17	☐ 34	☐ 57	☐ 85
Hastings	☐ 13	☐ 26	☐ 44	☐ 67	Beckman	☐ 8	☐ 37	☐ 54	☐ 72
Vitek	☐ 33	☐ 47	☐ 66	☐ 84		☐ 96			

$1.50 each

☐ 5 Goforth	☐ 29 Wildman	☐ 56 Trent	☐ 79 Halldorson
☐ 7 Lewis	☐ 30 Dixon	☐ 59 Vernon	☐ 80 Stephens
☐ 9 Wilson	☐ 31 Halldorson	☐ 60 Hill	☐ 81 Roberts
☐ 10 Caine	☐ 36 McKay	☐ 62 Hallston	☐ 82 Dailey
☐ 11 Vernon	☐ 39 Sinclair	☐ 63 Brent	☐ 83 Halston
☐ 14 Oliver	☐ 41 Owen	☐ 69 St. George	☐ 86 Adams
☐ 19 Thornton	☐ 42 Powers	☐ 70 Afton Bonds	☐ 89 James
☐ 20 Fulford	☐ 43 Robb	☐ 71 Ripy	☐ 90 Major
☐ 21 Richards	☐ 45 Carroll	☐ 74 Trent	☐ 92 McKay
☐ 22 Stephens	☐ 48 Wildman	☐ 75 Carroll	☐ 95 Wisdom
☐ 23 Edwards	☐ 49 Wisdom	☐ 76 Hardy	☐ 97 Clay
☐ 24 Healy	☐ 50 Scott	☐ 77 Cork	☐ 98 St. George
	☐ 55 Ladame	☐ 78 Oliver	☐ 99 Camp

$1.75 each

☐ 100 Stanford	☐ 105 Eden	☐ 110 Trent	☐ 115 John
☐ 101 Hardy	☐ 106 Dailey	☐ 111 South	☐ 116 Lindley
☐ 102 Hastings	☐ 107 Bright	☐ 112 Stanford	☐ 117 Scott
☐ 103 Cork	☐ 108 Hampson	☐ 113 Browning	☐ 118 Dailey
☐ 104 Vitek	☐ 109 Vernon	☐ 114 Michaels	☐ 119 Hampson

Silhouette Romance

Coming next month from
Silhouette Romances

Daring Encounter by Patti Beckman

Glamour, daring, mystique . . . Lord Richard Templeton
had them all. And it was up to Andria to make America's
top race idol an offer he couldn't refuse.

Devotion by Anne Hampson

Caryl's harmless masquerade backfired when Brad
proposed to the wrong girl! Could she ever reveal herself
and win his heart for her own?

Time Remembered by Lee Sawyer

His family had sent her father into bankruptcy years ago.
But Sabrina couldn't deny the passion that engulfed her
when Jules took her into his arms.

Game of Chance by Donna Vitek

Jason was everything Kit had ever hoped for, except that
he was a gambler. Could she accept his profession, or
would she lose the gamble—and his love?

An Ocean Of Love by Elizabeth Reynolds

He called her a gold digger and a fraud! Then suddenly,
his attitude changed, and Jill found herself passionately in
love with a man she didn't even like.

Yesterday's Bride by Susan Tracy

After years of separation, Leigh wanted to avoid seeing
Jason again. But he lured her into his turbulent world, for
she was his *wife*!

**Look for *Search For Love* by Nora Roberts
Available in July.**

READERS' COMMENTS ON SILHOUETTE ROMANCES:

"I would like to congratulate you on the most wonderful books I've had the pleasure of reading. They are a tremendous joy to those of us who have yet to meet the man of our dreams. From reading your books I quite truly believe that he will someday appear before me like a prince!"

—L.L.*, Hollandale, MS

"Your books are great, wholesome fiction, always with an upbeat, happy ending. Thank you."

—M.D., Massena, NY

"My boyfriend always teases me about Silhouette Books. He asks me, how's my love life and naturally I say terrific, but I tell him that there is always room for a little more romance from Silhouette."

—F.N., Ontario, Canada

"I would like to sincerely express my gratitude to you and your staff for bringing the pleasure of your publications to my attention. Your books are well written, mature and very contemporary."

—D.D., Staten Island, NY

*names available on request